WHO WANTS TO BE A
FOOTBALL MILLIONAIRE
WHO WANTS TO BE A™

WHO WANTS TO BE A

FOOTBALL MILLIONAIRE

WHO WANTS TO BE A™

QUIZ BOOK

HODDER

First published in Great Britain in 2010 by Hodder & Stoughton
An Hachette UK company

1

A CIP catalogue record for this title is available from the British Library.

ISBN 978 1 444 71063 2

Typeset in Verdana by Palimpsest Book Production Ltd,
Grangemouth, Stirlingshire

Printed and bound by Clays Ltd, St Ives plc

Hodder & Stoughton policy is to use papers that are natural, renewable and recyclable products and made from wood grown in sustainable forests. The logging and manufacturing processes are expected to conform to the environmental regulations of the country of origin.

Hodder & Stoughton Ltd
338 Euston Road
London NW1 3BH

www.hodder.co.uk

CONTENTS

How to play

Here's the ultimate challenge for all football fans and armchair contestants – 1,000 brain-teasing questions from the creators of *Who Wants To Be A Millionaire?* Picture the scene: you've won Fastest Finger First and now you're sitting in the hot-seat under the dimmed lights, ready to start your bid to climb the fifteen levels of the money tree to collect the virtual £1,000,000! You can challenge yourself, or invite some friends round and stage a tournament.

For 1 player

As on *Who Wants To Be A Millionaire?*, the aim of the game is to reach £1,000,000. Start with a question worth £100 and once you have decided on your final answer (and are absolutely sure . . .) follow the page reference at the foot of the page to find out if you've won that amount. If your answer is correct, you can play to win £200 and so on up the tree. The page where the £200 questions (and every other money level) begin is listed in the answer section.

As on the programme you have three lifelines to help you on your way to £1,000,000; these are, of course, optional but each of them can only be used once, so only use them when you really need to.

Fifty-Fifty

This option takes away two incorrect answers leaving the correct answer and one incorrect answer remaining, a page reference at the bottom of each page will direct you to the relevant section.

Ask The Audience

This lifeline tells you the percentage of the audience who think each answer is correct, a page reference at the bottom of each page will direct you to the relevant section.

Phone-A-Friend

If you have a telephone handy (and a willing friend!) ring him/her to help you out. You have thirty seconds (no cheating now . . .) to read the question to your friend and for them to tell you what they think the answer is. If there's someone else around, ask if they can time it for you.

If you answer incorrectly, you are out of the game. £1,000 and £32,000 are 'safe havens' so if you answer a question incorrectly and you have not reached £1,000 then not only are you out of the game but you won't have won a penny! If you have reached one (or both) of these havens and you answer a question incorrectly, then you are out of the game but you will have won the value of the previous haven you have reached. If at any point during the game you are unsure of an answer and don't want to risk losing everything if you answer incorrectly, you can walk away with the amount you have won so far and that will be your final score. Use the score sheets at the back of the book as you play to keep a running record of the amount you have won and the lifeline you have used.

For 2-5 players

Players should take turns at being the host and posing questions to the other contestant/s. The rules are the same as for a single player (see above). The game is over when everyone is out or when someone wins £1,000,000. The first person to reach £1,000,000 wins the game. If no one becomes a millionaire then the player who has won the most money when everyone is out is the winner.

Are you ready to play? Good luck and be sure to remember at all times the motto of *Who Wants To Be A Millionaire?* – it's only easy if you know the answer!

50:50

15	£1 MILLION
14	£5000,00
13	£250,000
12	£125,000
11	£64,000
10	£32,000
9	£16,000
8	£8,000
7	£4,000
6	£2,000
5	£1,000
4	£500
3	£300
2	£200
1	£100

1 ◆ £100 WORLD CUP

1

What appears on France's World Cup shirts?

- A: Beret
- B: Onion
- C: Cockerel
- D: Garlic bulb

2

Prior to 2010, how many African nations have won the World Cup?

- A: None
- B: One
- C: Two
- D: Three

3

Which of the following cities was not a 2006 World Cup finals venue?

- A: Hamburg
- B: Munich
- C: Cologne
- D: Amsterdam

4

Who captained the German team in the 2002 final?

- A: Oliver Stone
- B: Oliver Hardy
- C: Oliver Twist
- D: Oliver Kahn

If you would like to use your 50:50 please turn to page 289
If you would like to use your Ask The Audience please turn to page 313
Turn to the answer section on page 329 to find out if you've won £100!

1 ◆ £100 WORLD CUP

5

The World Cup normally takes place every . . .?

- A: Year
- B: Two years
- C: Three years
- D: Four years

6

Which team topped Group E at the 2006 tournament?

- A: Mali
- B: Ghana
- C: Italy
- D: USA

7

Which 2010 qualifiers are nicknamed the 'Socceroos'?

- A: Germany
- B: Ghana
- C: South Korea
- D: Australia

8

Which 2010 qualifiers are nicknamed the 'Desert Foxes'?

- A: Switzerland
- B: France
- C: Denmark
- D: Algeria

If you would like to use your 50:50 please turn to page 289
If you would like to use your Ask The Audience please turn to page 313
Turn to the answer section on page 329 to find out if you've won £100!

1 ◆ £100 WORLD CUP

9

Who or what went missing in the run-up to the 1966 World Cup finals?

- A: Russian linesman
- B: Jules Rimet trophy
- C: Wembley turf
- D: Bobby Charlton

10

What is traditionally presented to the winners of the World Cup?

- A: Brit Award
- B: Victoria Cross
- C: Oscar
- D: World Cup trophy

11

Which appropriately named player was part of the 1966 England World Cup squad?

- A: Dick Shinpad
- B: Bobby Cornerflag
- C: Geoff Offside
- D: Alan Ball

12

In which stadium did England win the 1966 World Cup final?

- A: Willesden
- B: West Ruislip
- C: Wembley
- D: Walford

If you would like to use your 50:50 please turn to page 289
If you would like to use your Ask The Audience please turn to page 313
Turn to the answer section on page 329 to find out if you've won £100!

1 ♦ £100 WORLD CUP

13

For which country did the female star Sun Wen play World Cup football?

- A: England
- B: Wales
- C: USA
- D: China

14

What is the first name of the Italian World Cup-winning captain Cannavaro?

- A: Terrifico
- B: Magnifico
- C: Fabio
- D: Wonderoso

15

In 2006, both the third and fourth-placed teams came from which continent?

- A: Asia
- B: Australasia
- C: Africa
- D: Europe

16

What decided the outcome of the 2006 final?

- A: Penalty shoot-out
- B: Coin toss
- C: National vote
- D: FIFA ruling

If you would like to use your 50:50 please turn to page 289
If you would like to use your Ask The Audience please turn to page 313
Turn to the answer section on page 329 to find out if you've won £100!

17

The 2002 tournament was hosted by South Korea and which other country?

- A: France
- B: Brazil
- C: Japan
- D: Sweden

18

Which of these is a nickname given to the World Cup star Pelé?

- A: Black Dog
- B: Black Cloud
- C: Black Spot
- D: Black Pearl

19

What is the first name of the English World Cup player Beckham?

- A: Michael
- B: Peter
- C: Bobby
- D: David

20

In which language is the World Cup known as the 'Coupe de monde'?

- A: Portuguese
- B: Italian
- C: Dutch
- D: French

If you would like to use your 50:50 please turn to page 289
If you would like to use your Ask The Audience please turn to page 313
Turn to the answer section on page 329 to find out if you've won £100!

1 ◆ £100 WORLD CUP

21

How many times has The Netherlands hosted the World Cup finals?

- A: Never
- B: Once
- C: Twice
- D: Three times

22

Ossie Ardiles, Gabriel Batistuta and Diego Maradona played World Cup football for which team?

- A: Spain
- B: Belgium
- C: Argentina
- D: The Netherlands

23

Marco van Basten, Marc Overmars and Jaap Stam played World Cup football for which team?

- A: The Netherlands
- B: Japan
- C: Cameroon
- D: Portugal

24

Franz Beckenbauer, Rudi Völler and Berti Vogts all played World Cup football for which team?

- A: England
- B: Germany
- C: Argentina
- D: Brazil

If you would like to use your 50:50 please turn to page 289
If you would like to use your Ask The Audience please turn to page 313
Turn to the answer section on page 329 to find out if you've won £100!

1 ◆ £100 WORLD CUP

25

Zagallo, Zico and Zizinho all made World Cup appearances for which team?

- A: Croatia
- B: Turkey
- C: Brazil
- D: Ghana

26

Prior to 2010, how many times have Italy won the World Cup?

- A: Never
- B: Once
- C: Four times
- D: Eight times

27

Prior to 2010, how many times have Brazil won the World Cup?

- A: Never
- B: Once
- C: Five times
- D: Ten times

28

Which of these teams did not qualify for the 2010 tournament from the African confederation?

- A: Algeria
- B: Honduras
- C: Cameroon
- D: Ghana

If you would like to use your 50:50 please turn to page 289
If you would like to use your Ask The Audience please turn to page 313
Turn to the answer section on page 329 to find out if you've won £100!

1 ◆ £100 WORLD CUP

29

Which was the only team from Oceania to qualify for the 2006 finals?

- A: Argentina
- B: Greece
- C: Brazil
- D: Australia

30

How many groups were there at the 2006 World Cup finals?

- A: Two
- B: Four
- C: Six
- D: Eight

31

At the 2006 World Cup finals, twelve teams wore shirts made by which company?

- A: Jaguar
- B: Cheetah
- C: Leopard
- D: Puma

32

Michel Platini, Just Fontaine and Thierry Henry have played World Cup football for which team?

- A: Spain
- B: England
- C: Italy
- D: France

If you would like to use your 50:50 please turn to page 289
If you would like to use your Ask The Audience please turn to page 313
Turn to the answer section on page 329 to find out if you've won £100!

1 ◆ £100 WORLD CUP

33

In 2006, what predominant colour were the first-choice shirts worn by the Czech Republic and Spain?

- A: Blue
- B: Yellow
- C: Red
- D: Green

34

At the 2006 World Cup, what colour were The Netherland's first-choice shirts?

- A: Blue
- B: Red
- C: Green
- D: Orange

35

Which 2010 qualifiers are nicknamed the 'Tigers of Asia'?

- A: South Korea
- B: Serbia
- C: Slovakia
- D: Switzerland

36

Which 2010 qualifying team has been dubbed the 'Olsen Gang'?

- A: Slovakia
- B: Japan
- C: Cameroon
- D: Denmark

If you would like to use your 50:50 please turn to page 289
If you would like to use your Ask The Audience please turn to page 313
Turn to the answer section on page 329 to find out if you've won £100!

1 ◆ £100 WORLD CUP

37

In 1950, which team became the second to win the World Cup twice?

- A: England
- B: Scotland
- C: Wales
- D: Uruguay

38

In 1998, France v Paraguay was the first World Cup finals match to be settled by which method?

- A: Silver shot
- B: Golden goal
- C: Platinum penalty
- D: Copper corner

39

Under the laws of the game, which one of the following is not compulsory equipment for a player in a World Cup match?

- A: Shorts
- B: Socks
- C: Shinguards
- D: Sunglasses

40

Which of these is an award given to the top goalscorer at the World Cup finals?

- A: Golden Stud
- B: Golden Shoe
- C: Golden Forehead
- D: Golden Shinpad

If you would like to use your 50:50 please turn to page 289
If you would like to use your Ask The Audience please turn to page 313
Turn to the answer section on page 329 to find out if you've won £100!

1 ◆ £100 WORLD CUP

41

What method is used to decide World Cup matches if teams are drawn after extra time?

- A: Charades
- B: Penalties
- C: Conkers
- D: Quiz questions

42

What do teams try to score in order to win matches at the World Cup?

- A: Touchdowns
- B: Baskets
- C: Goals
- D: Tries

43

Which team topped Group H at the 2006 tournament?

- A: Tunisia
- B: Spain
- C: Saudi Arabia
- D: Ukraine

44

Who was the top scorer at the 1938 World Cup finals?

- A: Adidas
- B: Davidas
- C: Disordas
- D: Leonidas

If you would like to use your 50:50 please turn to page 289
If you would like to use your Ask The Audience please turn to page 313
Turn to the answer section on page 329 to find out if you've won £100!

1 ◆ £100 WORLD CUP

45

Who scored Brazil's two goals in the 2002 final against Germany?

- A: Williamo
- B: Johno
- C: Ronaldo
- D: Franko

46

In which language is the World Cup tournament known as 'Campionato mondiale di calcio'?

- A: Arabic
- B: English
- C: Italian
- D: French

47

By what name were the Hungarian team that competed in the 1954 World Cup known?

- A: Mighty Mice
- B: Mighty Muppets
- C: Mighty Men
- D: Mighty Magyars

48

What three letters appear on the badge on Brazil's World Cup shirts?

- A: SSS
- B: CBF
- C: ZZZ
- D: SOS

If you would like to use your 50:50 please turn to page 289
If you would like to use your Ask The Audience please turn to page 313
Turn to the answer section on page 329 to find out if you've won £100!

49

Who captained the England team at the 2002 World Cup?

- A: David Baddiel
- B: David Brent
- C: David Blunkett
- D: David Beckham

50

What is the name of the US stadium that was the venue of the 1994 World Cup final?

- A: Tea Cup
- B: Coffee Pot
- C: Rose Bowl
- D: Flower Vase

If you would like to use your 50:50 please turn to page 289
If you would like to use your Ask The Audience please turn to page 313
Turn to the answer section on page 329 to find out if you've won £100!

1 ◆ £100 EUROPEAN

1

Who would not play in the top flight of Spanish football?

- A: Real Madrid
- B: Barcelona
- C: Valencia
- D: Borussia Dortmund

2

What does the 'Bayern' refer to in the name Bayern Munich?

- A: Brazil
- B: Botswana
- C: Belgium
- D: Bavaria

3

The Champions League is contested every . . . ?

- A: Year
- B: Two years
- C: Three years
- D: Four years

4

Which of these is a stadium in Paris, seating more than 80,000?

- A: Stade de Spain
- B: Stade d'Italy
- C: Stade de Portugal
- D: Stade de France

If you would like to use your 50:50 please turn to page 289
If you would like to use your Ask The Audience please turn to page 313
Turn to the answer section on page 329 to find out if you've won £100!

1 ◆ £100 EUROPEAN

5

How many teams are drawn in each of the eight groups in the Champions League?

- A: Four
- B: Ten
- C: Sixteen
- D: Twenty-four

6

Which tournament was abolished in the 1990s?

- A: Champions League
- B: UEFA Cup
- C: Europa League
- D: Cup Winners' Cup

7

Which of these trophies can a European football team not win?

- A: Ryder Cup
- B: Champions League
- C: European Super Cup
- D: Europa League

8

What letters precede Eindhoven to make the name of a famous Dutch club?

- A: CIA
- B: KGB
- C: SOS
- D: PSV

If you would like to use your 50:50 please turn to pages 289–290
If you would like to use your Ask The Audience please turn to page 313
Turn to the answer section on page 329 to find out if you've won £100!

1 ◆ £100 EUROPEAN

9

Which was an Italian Serie A team in the 2009/10 season?

- A: Benfica
- B: Feyenoord
- C: Juventus
- D: Bordeaux

10

What precedes Mönchengladbach to make the name of a well-known German club?

- A: Bayern
- B: Borussia
- C: Hertha
- D: Werder

11

Although not in Europe geographically, which of these is a member of UEFA?

- A: Japan
- B: South Africa
- C: Canada
- D: Israel

12

What is the colour of the first-choice shirts worn by the national teams of Scotland, Italy and France?

- A: Blue
- B: Yellow
- C: Orange
- D: Green

If you would like to use your 50:50 please turn to page 290
If you would like to use your Ask The Audience please turn to page 313
Turn to the answer section on page 329 to find out if you've won £100!

1 ◆ £100 EUROPEAN

13

What is the colour of the first-choice shirts worn by the national teams of Greece, Germany and England?

- A: Blue
- B: Yellow
- C: White
- D: Black

14

Which of these is the controlling body of European football?

- A: CIA
- B: ABBA
- C: UNESCO
- D: UEFA

15

Which of these teams would not compete in the Champions League?

- A: LA Galaxy
- B: Real Madrid
- C: Manchester United
- D: Juventus

16

During normal time in Euro 2008, Romania's Adrian Mutu was the only player to do what?

- A: Miss a penalty
- B: Take a free kick
- C: Take a throw-in
- D: Take a corner

If you would like to use your 50:50 please turn to page 290
If you would like to use your Ask The Audience please turn to page 314
Turn to the answer section on page 329 to find out if you've won £100!

1 ◆ £100 EUROPEAN

17

What name was given to the official match ball used at Euro 2008?

- A: Eurotunnel
- B: Europass
- C: Eurostar
- D: Eurovision

18

Which of these teams did not reach the finals stage of Euro 2008?

- A: Portugal
- B: Croatia
- C: The Netherlands
- D: Uruguay

19

Teams with the prefix Borussia play in the top flight of domestic football in which country?

- A: Germany
- B: Greece
- C: Malta
- D: Turkey

20

Dynamo Kiev, Obolon Kiev and Arsenal Kiev all play in which country?

- A: Ukraine
- B: Spain
- C: France
- D: Scotland

If you would like to use your 50:50 please turn to page 290
If you would like to use your Ask The Audience please turn to page 314
Turn to the answer section on page 329 to find out if you've won £100!

1 ◆ £100 EUROPEAN

21

When is the Champions League final played?

- A: Christmas Day
- B: New Year's Day
- C: August
- D: May

22

Which of these is a top-flight French league club?

- A: Montenegro
- B: Montypython
- C: Montpellier
- D: Montgomery

23

Whose hat-trick helped knock England out of the 1988 European Championship?

- A: Marco van Basten
- B: Dick van Dyke
- C: Vincent van Gogh
- D: Hertz van Rental

24

Complete the name of the famous Spanish club, Real . . .

- A: Madrid
- B: Munich
- C: Marseille
- D: Manchester

If you would like to use your 50:50 please turn to page 290
If you would like to use your Ask The Audience please turn to page 314
Turn to the answer section on page 329 to find out if you've won £100!

1 ◆ £100 EUROPEAN

25

Which of these teams has won the Champions League?

- A: Grenoble
- B: Real Madrid
- C: Tromso
- D: Grasshoppers

26

How are the groups for the Europa League identified?

- A: One to twelve
- B: Alpha to Mu
- C: A to L
- D: I to XII

27

'God Save The Queen' is played before which country's matches?

- A: France
- B: Germany
- C: England
- D: Russia

If you would like to use your 50:50 please turn to page 290
If you would like to use your Ask The Audience please turn to page 314
Turn to the answer section on page 329 to find out if you've won £100!

1 ◆ £100 DOMESTIC

1

Which team did Rangers not play against in their 2009/10 domestic season?

- A: Aberdeen
- B: Bolton Wanderers
- C: Celtic
- D: Dundee United

2

Which club did Sven-Göran Eriksson join in 2009 as its Director of Football?

- A: Derby County
- B: Stockport County
- C: Ross County
- D: Notts County

3

Which is the only English city beginning with a 'W' to have a 2009/10 Premier League club?

- A: Wolverhampton
- B: Winchester
- C: Wakefield
- D: Worcester

4

Which of these clubs plays home games in its country's capital city?

- A: Everton
- B: Swansea City
- C: Hibernian
- D: Aston Villa

If you would like to use your 50:50 please turn to page 290
If you would like to use your Ask The Audience please turn to page 314
Turn to the answer section on page 329 to find out if you've won £100!

1 ◆ £100 DOMESTIC

5

Which of these is not a popular component of English and Scottish club names?

- A: United
- B: City
- C: Scoundrels
- D: Town

6

Who brought a lawsuit against Peterborough to stop them from registering the trademark 'Posh'?

- A: Joanna Lumley
- B: Michael Winner
- C: Victoria Beckham
- D: The Queen

7

What is the nickname of Hull City, based on their original black and orange striped strip?

- A: The Zebras
- B: The Camels
- C: The Panthers
- D: The Tigers

8

What day of the week follows Sheffield to give the name of an English league club?

- A: Monday
- B: Tuesday
- C: Wednesday
- D: Thursday

If you would like to use your 50:50 please turn to page 290
If you would like to use your Ask The Audience please turn to page 314
Turn to the answer section on page 329 to find out if you've won £100!

1 ◆ £100 DOMESTIC

9

Derby County's former home ground was originally used for what sport?

- A: Baseball
- B: Volleyball
- C: Basketball
- D: Stoolball

10

What nationality are George Gillett and Tom Hicks who gained control of Liverpool in 2007?

- A: Russian
- B: British
- C: American
- D: Australian

11

What term is used when a top team is knocked out of a cup competition by a team from the lower divisions?

- A: Giant killing
- B: Fly swatting
- C: Bug crushing
- D: Dragon slaying

12

Which of these managed England in the 1970s?

- A: Don McLean
- B: Don Corleone
- C: Don Johnson
- D: Don Revie

If you would like to use your 50:50 please turn to page 290
If you would like to use your Ask The Audience please turn to page 314
Turn to the answer section on page 329 to find out if you've won £100!

1 ◆ £100 DOMESTIC

13

Which of these is a former Liverpool, Leeds United and England forward?

- A: Robbie Tripper
- B: Robbie Fowler
- C: Robbie Shover
- D: Robbie Offender

14

England normally play their home international matches on what surface?

- A: Gravel
- B: Concrete
- C: Grass
- D: Astroturf

15

Who played in just one international for England, against Ireland in 1910?

- A: Albert Hall
- B: Hyde Park
- C: Tate Modern
- D: Marble Arch

16

What is the name of the Welsh national stadium?

- A: Eon Stadium
- B: Millennium Stadium
- C: Century Stadium
- D: Decade Stadium

If you would like to use your 50:50 please turn to page 290
If you would like to use your Ask The Audience please turn to page 314
Turn to the answer section on page 329 to find out if you've won £100!

1 ◆ £100 DOMESTIC

17

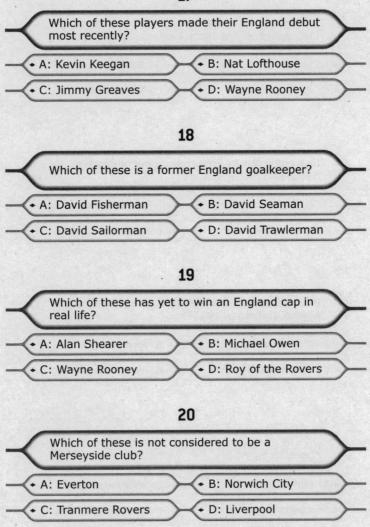

Which of these players made their England debut most recently?

- A: Kevin Keegan
- B: Nat Lofthouse
- C: Jimmy Greaves
- D: Wayne Rooney

18

Which of these is a former England goalkeeper?

- A: David Fisherman
- B: David Seaman
- C: David Sailorman
- D: David Trawlerman

19

Which of these has yet to win an England cap in real life?

- A: Alan Shearer
- B: Michael Owen
- C: Wayne Rooney
- D: Roy of the Rovers

20

Which of these is not considered to be a Merseyside club?

- A: Everton
- B: Norwich City
- C: Tranmere Rovers
- D: Liverpool

If you would like to use your 50:50 please turn to page 290
If you would like to use your Ask The Audience please turn to page 314
Turn to the answer section on page 329 to find out if you've won £100!

1 ◆ £100 DOMESTIC

21

What follows Newcastle, West Ham and Sheffield in the names of the three football clubs?

- A: Rovers
- B: Athletic
- C: City
- D: United

22

What emblem has appeared on every England shirt since 1872?

- A: Three dogs
- B: Three elephants
- C: Three bears
- D: Three lions

23

Which of these managers did not represent England at international level?

- A: Terry Venables
- B: Kevin Keegan
- C: Glenn Hoddle
- D: Sven-Göran Eriksson

24

Which of these regularly played in goal for England?

- A: Ray Winstone
- B: Ray Davies
- C: Ray Clemence
- D: Ray Charles

If you would like to use your 50:50 please turn to page 290
If you would like to use your Ask The Audience please turn to page 314
Turn to the answer section on page 329 to find out if you've won £100!

1 ◆ £100 DOMESTIC

25

In terms of winning the league title, which is England's most successful city?

- A: Bristol
- B: Sheffield
- C: Leeds
- D: Liverpool

26

Complete the name of the Scottish club, Hamilton . . .

- A: Professorial
- B: Philosophical
- C: Academical
- D: Tutorial

27

Who were the only Premier League 'Rovers' in 2009/10?

- A: Blackburn
- B: Bristol
- C: Doncaster
- D: Tranmere

If you would like to use your 50:50 please turn to page 290
If you would like to use your Ask The Audience please turn to page 314
Turn to the answer section on page 329 to find out if you've won £100!

50:50

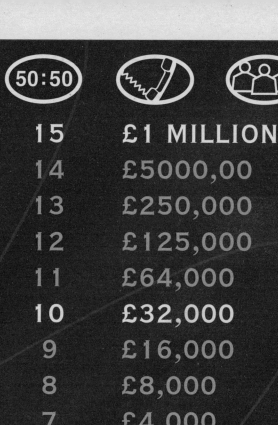

15	£1 MILLION
14	£5000,00
13	£250,000
12	£125,000
11	£64,000
10	£32,000
9	£16,000
8	£8,000
7	£4,000
6	£2,000
5	£1,000
4	£500
3	£300
2	£200
1	£100

2 ◆ £200 WORLD CUP

1

Which team topped Group B at the 2006 tournament?

- A: Sweden
- B: Paraguay
- C: England
- D: Trinidad & Tobago

2

What is the first name of the Argentinian World Cup star Maradona?

- A: Paolo
- B: Roberto
- C: Stefano
- D: Diego

3

Which of these countries has never hosted the tournament?

- A: Argentina
- B: Mexico
- C: Spain
- D: Iceland

4

How many points are given for a group win in the World Cup finals?

- A: Three
- B: Six
- C: Nine
- D: Twelve

If you would like to use your 50:50 please turn to page 291
If you would like to use your Ask The Audience please turn to page 314
Turn to the answer section on page 330 to find out if you've won £200!

2 ◆ £200 WORLD CUP

5

Which of these cities has never hosted a World Cup final?

- A: Paris
- B: London
- C: Los Angeles
- D: Plymouth

6

Who was named in England's initial 2006 squad, despite having never played in the Premiership?

- A: Thierry Henry
- B: Theo Walcott
- C: Alan Shearer
- D: Alan Hansen

7

What ended England's involvement in the 1990 and 1998 World Cup finals?

- A: Toss of a coin
- B: Arm wrestle
- C: Drawing straws
- D: Penalty shoot-out

8

Which item of clothing did Pelé swap with Bobby Moore after the England v Brazil match in 1970?

- A: Sock
- B: Shorts
- C: Hat
- D: Shirt

If you would like to use your 50:50 please turn to page 291
If you would like to use your Ask The Audience please turn to page 314
Turn to the answer section on page 330 to find out if you've won £200!

2 ◆ £200 WORLD CUP

9

Which World Cup winners are nicknamed the 'Samba Boys'?

- A: England
- B: France
- C: Brazil
- D: Germany

10

Which of these was selected for the USA's 2006 squad?

- A: Kelsey Grammer
- B: Casey Kasem
- C: Kasey Keller
- D: Chelsea Clinton

11

What was introduced at the 1998 World Cup to show stoppage time at the end of matches?

- A: Electronic display
- B: Flipcharts
- C: Chalkboards
- D: Clock chimes

12

Which team made their World Cup debut in 2006?

- A: Côte Ébène
- B: Côte d'Argent
- C: Côte d'Or
- D: Côte d'Ivoire

If you would like to use your 50:50 please turn to page 291
If you would like to use your Ask The Audience please turn to page 314
Turn to the answer section on page 330 to find out if you've won £200!

2 ◆ £200 WORLD CUP

13

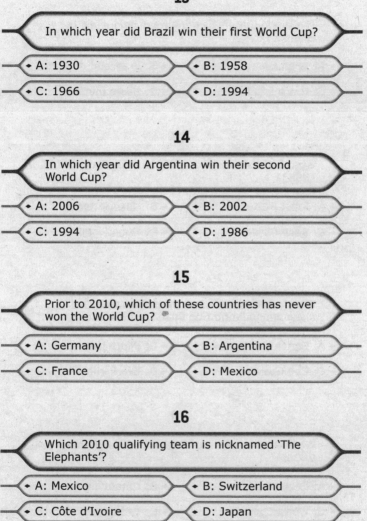

In which year did Brazil win their first World Cup?

- A: 1930
- B: 1958
- C: 1966
- D: 1994

14

In which year did Argentina win their second World Cup?

- A: 2006
- B: 2002
- C: 1994
- D: 1986

15

Prior to 2010, which of these countries has never won the World Cup?

- A: Germany
- B: Argentina
- C: France
- D: Mexico

16

Which 2010 qualifying team is nicknamed 'The Elephants'?

- A: Mexico
- B: Switzerland
- C: Côte d'Ivoire
- D: Japan

If you would like to use your 50:50 please turn to page 291
If you would like to use your Ask The Audience please turn to page 314
Turn to the answer section on page 330 to find out if you've won £200!

2 ◆ £200 WORLD CUP

17

The World Cup finals are always held when the year . . .

- A: Is an even number
- B: Is an odd number
- C: Has a 5 in it
- D: Has a 0 in it

18

What is the name of the FIFA president elected in 1998?

- A: Ernst Flatter
- B: Max Clatter
- C: Sepp Blatter
- D: Hugo Platter

19

Who famously wore the number 10 shirt for Argentina in World Cup finals?

- A: Carlos Menem
- B: Diego Maradona
- C: Che Guevara
- D: Eva Peron

20

What was the name of England's 1966 World Cup mascot?

- A: England Eddie
- B: London Lenny
- C: World Cup Willie
- D: Wembley Wilf

If you would like to use your 50:50 please turn to page 291
If you would like to use your Ask The Audience please turn to page 314
Turn to the answer section on page 330 to find out if you've won £200!

2 ◆ £200 WORLD CUP

21

Which of the following played a part in England's 1990 World Cup campaign?

- A: Chris Waddle
- B: Colin Swagger
- C: Clive Shuffle
- D: Clint Strutting

22

In 2006, the winners and runners-up both came from which continent?

- A: Africa
- B: Europe
- C: Asia
- D: South America

23

Who captained Italy to their fourth World Cup title in 2006?

- A: Canaletto
- B: Caravaggio
- C: Cannavaro
- D: Correggio

24

Which French captain was sensationally sent off during the 2006 final?

- A: Thierry Henry
- B: Patrick Vieira
- C: Frank Ribery
- D: Zinedine Zidane

If you would like to use your 50:50 please turn to page 291
If you would like to use your Ask The Audience please turn to page 314
Turn to the answer section on page 330 to find out if you've won £200!

2 ◆ £200 WORLD CUP

25

In which of these years was the final played in the Olympiastadion in Berlin?

- A: 1930
- B: 1966
- C: 2002
- D: 2006

26

In which year was the World Cup final played in the International Stadium in Yokohama?

- A: 1966
- B: 1998
- C: 2002
- D: 2006

27

What is the first name on the birth certificate of the Brazilian World Cup legend Pelé?

- A: Watson
- B: Edison
- C: Robson
- D: Jackson

28

In which language is the World Cup known as 'Die Weltmeisterschaft'?

- A: Spanish
- B: Greek
- C: Swedish
- D: German

If you would like to use your 50:50 please turn to page 291
If you would like to use your Ask The Audience please turn to page 314–315
Turn to the answer section on page 330 to find out if you've won £200!

2 ◆ £200 WORLD CUP

29

Slaven Bilic, Mario Stanic and Davor Suker played World Cup football for which team?

- A: Greece
- B: Sweden
- C: Croatia
- D: Russia

30

Which of these nicknames has not been given to the Dutch national team?

- A: The Orangemen
- B: Clockwork Orange
- C: Oranje
- D: Chocolate Orange

31

What is the full first name of the German World Cup finalist Rudi Völler?

- A: Rudyard
- B: Rudiger
- C: Rudd
- D: Rudolf

32

Eusébio, Cristiano Ronaldo and Tiago have played World Cup football for which team?

- A: Spain
- B: Brazil
- C: Portugal
- D: Argentina

If you would like to use your 50:50 please turn to page 291
If you would like to use your Ask The Audience please turn to page 315
Turn to the answer section on page 330 to find out if you've won £200!

2 ◆ £200 WORLD CUP

33

Johan Cruyff, Dennis Bergkamp and Frank de Boer played World Cup football for which team?

- A: The Netherlands
- B: Sweden
- C: Germany
- D: Switzerland

34

Dida, Didi and Dunga all made World Cup appearances for which team?

- A: Portugal
- B: Sweden
- C: Argentina
- D: Brazil

35

How many times have Brazil not appeared in the World Cup finals?

- A: Never
- B: Twice
- C: Three times
- D: Four times

36

Which of these teams did not make the quarter-finals of the 2006 tournament?

- A: Portugal
- B: Brazil
- C: The Netherlands
- D: France

If you would like to use your 50:50 please turn to page 291
If you would like to use your Ask The Audience please turn to page 315
Turn to the answer section on page 330 to find out if you've won £200!

2 ◆ £200 WORLD CUP

37

Which of these countries did not qualify for 2010 from the South American confederation?

- A: USA
- B: Argentina
- C: Chile
- D: Uruguay

38

At the 2006 World Cup finals, an image of what animal appeared on the Côte d'Ivoire shirts?

- A: Kangaroo
- B: Elephant
- C: Wallaby
- D: Crocodile

39

At the 2006 World Cup finals, what colour were Brazil's first-choice shirts?

- A: Blue
- B: Red
- C: Yellow
- D: Green

40

Which national football team are known as 'Die Nationalmannschaft'?

- A: Portugal
- B: Spain
- C: Germany
- D: The Netherlands

If you would like to use your 50:50 please turn to page 291
If you would like to use your Ask The Audience please turn to page 315
Turn to the answer section on page 330 to find out if you've won £200!

2 ◆ £200 WORLD CUP

41

Which was the first team to win the World Cup for a second time?

- A: USA
- B: Romania
- C: Switzerland
- D: Italy

42

The 1994 World Cup final was the first to have what?

- A: No yellow cards
- B: No substitutes used
- C: No red cards
- D: Penalty shoot-out

43

Which of these did England win at the 1990 World Cup finals?

- A: Fair Play award
- B: Jules Rimet trophy
- C: Italian lottery
- D: Wooden spoon

44

In which of these years did the host country not win the World Cup?

- A: 1930
- B: 1934
- C: 1966
- D: 2002

If you would like to use your 50:50 please turn to page 291
If you would like to use your Ask The Audience please turn to page 315
Turn to the answer section on page 330 to find out if you've won £200!

2 ◆ £200 WORLD CUP

45

Complete the name of the Argentinian 1974 World Cup player Roberto.

- A: Odoroso
- B: Cologno
- C: Aromo
- D: Perfumo

46

What is 'Ossie' short for in the name of the Argentinian World Cup star Ossie Ardiles?

- A: Osborne
- B: Osrick
- C: Oscar
- D: Osvaldo

47

Which of these teams did not qualify for 2010 from CONCACAF?

- A: USA
- B: Honduras
- C: Brazil
- D: Mexico

48

In 2006, Argentina defeated which team 6-0?

- A: Italy
- B: Serbia & Montenegro
- C: Germany
- D: Brazil

If you would like to use your 50:50 please turn to page 291
If you would like to use your Ask The Audience please turn to page 315
Turn to the answer section on page 330 to find out if you've won £200!

2 ◆ £200 WORLD CUP

49

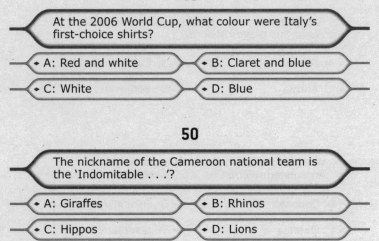

At the 2006 World Cup, what colour were Italy's first-choice shirts?

- A: Red and white
- B: Claret and blue
- C: White
- D: Blue

50

The nickname of the Cameroon national team is the 'Indomitable . . .'?

- A: Giraffes
- B: Rhinos
- C: Hippos
- D: Lions

If you would like to use your 50:50 please turn to page 291
If you would like to use your Ask The Audience please turn to page 315
Turn to the answer section on page 330 to find out if you've won £200!

2 ◆ £200 EUROPEAN

1

In which city is the Italian club Internazionale based?

- A: Rome
- B: Venice
- C: Parma
- D: Milan

2

Black and white striped shirts are most associated with which of these clubs?

- A: Juventus
- B: Real Madrid
- C: Benfica
- D: Bayern Munich

3

Who would hear a rendition of 'La Marseillaise' before playing for his country?

- A: Michael Ballack
- B: Thierry Henry
- C: Filippo Inzaghi
- D: Xabi Alonso

4

In which domestic league would Juventus play Lazio?

- A: Ligue 1
- B: Bundesliga
- C: Eredivisie
- D: Serie A

If you would like to use your 50:50 please turn to page 291
If you would like to use your Ask The Audience please turn to page 315
Turn to the answer section on page 330 to find out if you've won £200!

2 ◆ £200 EUROPEAN

5

Which European country plays its domestic league season from March to October?

- A: Sweden
- B: Portugal
- C: Spain
- D: Italy

6

Yellow shirts are part of the first-choice strip of which country's national team?

- A: France
- B: Germany
- C: Sweden
- D: Italy

7

Olympiakos and Panathinaikos play their domestic football in which country?

- A: Finland
- B: Austria
- C: Greece
- D: Poland

8

Lech Poznan, Lechia Gdansk and Piast Gliwice are clubs from which country?

- A: Poland
- B: Portugal
- C: Ireland
- D: Belgium

If you would like to use your 50:50 please turn to page 291
If you would like to use your Ask The Audience please turn to page 315
Turn to the answer section on page 330 to find out if you've won £200!

2 ◆ £200 EUROPEAN

9

A stylized Eiffel Tower appears on the badge of which French club?

- A: Lille
- B: Toulouse
- C: Paris Saint-Germain
- D: Lens

10

Which club is not based in its national capital?

- A: Real Madrid
- B: Paris Saint-Germain
- C: Sparta Prague
- D: Inter Milan

11

After which player was a ruling regarding international transfers named in 1995?

- A: Jean-Marc Bosman
- B: Thierry Henry
- C: Oliver Kahn
- D: David Beckham

12

The Italian Serie A title has never been won by which team?

- A: Lazio
- B: Inter Milan
- C: Juventus
- D: Barcelona

If you would like to use your 50:50 please turn to page 291
If you would like to use your Ask The Audience please turn to page 315
Turn to the answer section on page 330 to find out if you've won £200!

2 ◆ £200 EUROPEAN

13

Which of these does not precede Moscow to give the name of a Russian club?

- A: CSKA
- B: Dynamo
- C: Bayern
- D: Locomotive

14

Chievo, Udinese and Lazio are 2009/10 top-flight teams in which country?

- A: Poland
- B: Italy
- C: Ukraine
- D: Finland

15

Who never scored a goal for his country in his international career?

- A: Johan Cruyff
- B: Dennis Bergkamp
- C: Dino Zoff
- D: George Best

16

Which of these would be an international match between neighbouring countries?

- A: Greece v Portugal
- B: Italy v France
- C: Hungary v Republic of Ireland
- D: Finland v Spain

If you would like to use your 50:50 please turn to pages 291–292
If you would like to use your Ask The Audience please turn to page 315
Turn to the answer section on page 330 to find out if you've won £200!

2 ◆ £200 EUROPEAN

17

In which city would Spain play home internationals?

- A: Munich
- B: Manchester
- C: Minsk
- D: Madrid

18

Which of these fixtures would involve the away team crossing the North Sea?

- A: Portugal v France
- B: Italy v Cyprus
- C: Scotland v Denmark
- D: Russia v Poland

19

Who has won over 100 caps for Germany?

- A: Paolo Maldini
- B: Cristiano Ronaldo
- C: Gary Lineker
- D: Jürgen Klinsmann

20

What is the predominant colour of the home shirts worn by The Netherlands?

- A: Green
- B: Pink
- C: Orange
- D: Black

If you would like to use your 50:50 please turn to page 292
If you would like to use your Ask The Audience please turn to page 315
Turn to the answer section on page 330 to find out if you've won £200!

2 ◆ £200 EUROPEAN

21

Which word precedes Santander to give the name of a top Spanish club?

- A: Sporting
- B: Shooting
- C: Running
- D: Racing

22

For which country does the forward Birgit Prinz play?

- A: Germany
- B: England
- C: Ireland
- D: USA

23

Which of these islands is a member of UEFA?

- A: Iceland
- B: Jamaica
- C: Madagascar
- D: Newfoundland

24

What is the colour of the first-choice shirts worn by the national teams of Norway, Belgium and Spain?

- A: Green
- B: Black
- C: Red
- D: Gold

If you would like to use your 50:50 please turn to page 292
If you would like to use your Ask The Audience please turn to page 315
Turn to the answer section on page 330 to find out if you've won £200!

2 ◆ £200 EUROPEAN

25

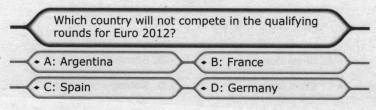

Which country will not compete in the qualifying rounds for Euro 2012?

◆ A: Argentina
◆ B: France
◆ C: Spain
◆ D: Germany

If you would like to use your 50:50 please turn to page 292
If you would like to use your Ask The Audience please turn to page 315
Turn to the answer section on page 330 to find out if you've won £200!

2 ◆ £200 DOMESTIC

1

Who bought Chelsea FC in 2003?

- A: Silvio Berlusconi
- B: Bernie Ecclestone
- C: Elton John
- D: Roman Abramovich

2

In 1986, Alex Ferguson took over as the manager of which club?

- A: Leeds United
- B: West Ham United
- C: Sheffield United
- D: Manchester United

3

What is the most common name in use by clubs in the English and Scottish leagues?

- A: Wanderers
- B: Albion
- C: Athletic
- D: United

4

The song 'I'm Forever Blowing Bubbles' is associated with which club?

- A: Stoke City
- B: Everton
- C: Liverpool
- D: West Ham United

If you would like to use your 50:50 please turn to page 292
If you would like to use your Ask The Audience please turn to page 315
Turn to the answer section on page 330 to find out if you've won £200!

2 ◆ £200 DOMESTIC

5

With which other Edinburgh club does Hibernian have a fierce local rivalry?

- A: Hearts
- B: St Mirren
- C: Motherwell
- D: Hamilton

6

Which crisp manufacturer has had a long association with Leicester City?

- A: McCoys
- B: Smith's
- C: Golden Wonder
- D: Walkers

7

How was the second tier of the English League known before the introduction of the Premiership?

- A: Tier Two
- B: Level Two
- C: Division Two
- D: League Two

8

By what name is the former Charity Shield now known?

- A: Community Shield
- B: Fellowship Shield
- C: Civic Shield
- D: Neighbourhood Shield

If you would like to use your 50:50 please turn to page 292
If you would like to use your Ask The Audience please turn to page 315
Turn to the answer section on page 330 to find out if you've won £200!

2 ◆ £200 DOMESTIC

9

Which club were Scottish League champions for nine successive years from 1989-97?

- A: Rangers
- B: Dundee United
- C: Aberdeen
- D: Kilmarnock

10

Who surprisingly put Manchester United out of the 2009/10 FA Cup, winning 1-0 at Old Trafford?

- A: Colchester United
- B: Hereford United
- C: Leeds United
- D: Rotherham United

11

What follows Burton, West Bromwich and Brighton & Hove to give the names of three clubs?

- A: City
- B: United
- C: Albion
- D: Wanderers

12

An East Midlands derby might involve Leicester City and which of these?

- A: Leeds United
- B: Carlisle United
- C: Blackburn Rovers
- D: Derby County

If you would like to use your 50:50 please turn to page 292
If you would like to use your Ask The Audience please turn to page 315
Turn to the answer section on page 330 to find out if you've won £200!

2 ◆ £200 DOMESTIC

13

What two words go before Midlothian to give the name of a Scottish League club?

- A: Heart of
- B: Soul of
- C: Body of
- D: Spirit of

14

Which of these was an Arsenal, Middlesbrough and England midfielder?

- A: Ray Conservatory
- B: Ray Parlour
- C: Ray Lounge
- D: Ray Pantry

15

As which of these did Alan Shearer win sixty-three caps for England?

- A: Goalkeeper
- B: Defender
- C: Midfielder
- D: Striker

16

The England star Bobby Charlton gave his name to which hairstyle?

- A: Comb-over
- B: Up 'n' over
- C: Backcomb
- D: Rollover

If you would like to use your 50:50 please turn to page 292
If you would like to use your Ask The Audience please turn to page 315
Turn to the answer section on page 330 to find out if you've won £200!

2 ◆ £200 DOMESTIC

17

Which of the following is a feature of the new Wembley Stadium?

- A: Glass roof
- B: Tiled roof
- C: Sliding roof
- D: Thatched roof

18

Against which of these clubs would Chelsea not play a London derby match?

- A: Tottenham Hotspur
- B: Aston Villa
- C: Fulham
- D: Arsenal

19

Which England manager acquired the nickname 'El Tel' after a spell in charge at Barcelona?

- A: Bobby Robson
- B: Glenn Hoddle
- C: Terry Venables
- D: Sven-Göran Eriksson

20

In Scotland, the vast majority of league clubs have what word in the name of their ground?

- A: Lawn
- B: Garden
- C: Estate
- D: Park

If you would like to use your 50:50 please turn to page 292
If you would like to use your Ask The Audience please turn to page 315–316
Turn to the answer section on page 330 to find out if you've won £200!

2 ◆ £200 DOMESTIC

21

As of 2009, which club had won eighteen First Division titles but no Premiership titles?

- A: Manchester United
- B: Arsenal
- C: Blackburn Rovers
- D: Liverpool

22

Which of these is a former Liverpool and England midfielder?

- A: Steve Man
- B: Steve McMan
- C: Steve McManam
- D: Steve McManaman

23

What construction features in the name of Chelsea's home ground?

- A: Column
- B: Bridge
- C: Tower
- D: Archway

24

Supporters of which international team traditionally refer to England as 'the auld enemy'?

- A: Republic of Ireland
- B: Scotland
- C: France
- D: Argentina

If you would like to use your 50:50 please turn to page 292
If you would like to use your Ask The Audience please turn to page 316
Turn to the answer section on page 330 to find out if you've won £200!

2 ◆ £200 DOMESTIC

25

How does the motto of Tottenham Hotspur translate into English?

- A: London forever
- B: To dare is to do
- C: 4-3 again
- D: Oh no, not Arsenal

If you would like to use your 50:50 please turn to page 292
If you would like to use your Ask The Audience please turn to page 316
Turn to the answer section on page 330 to find out if you've won £200!

50:50

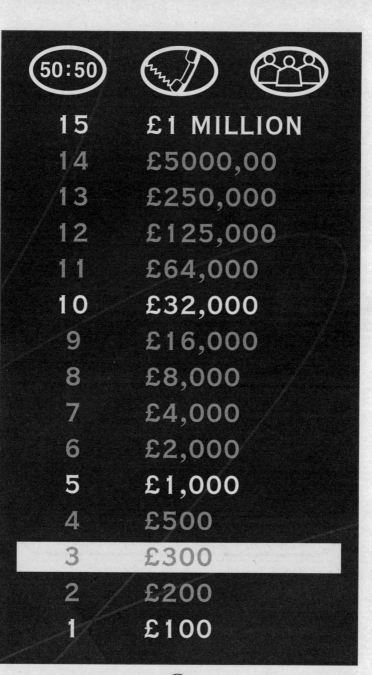

15	£1 MILLION
14	£5000,00
13	£250,000
12	£125,000
11	£64,000
10	£32,000
9	£16,000
8	£8,000
7	£4,000
6	£2,000
5	£1,000
4	£500
3	£300
2	£200
1	£100

3 ◆ £300 WORLD CUP

1

In which language is the World Cup known as the 'Copa del mundo'?

- A: French
- B: Spanish
- C: German
- D: Dutch

2

How many groups are there in the 2010 World Cup finals?

- A: Ten
- B: Six
- C: Eight
- D: Four

3

What is the nickname of the 2010 qualifiers Nigeria?

- A: Super Stars
- B: Supermen
- C: Super Eagles
- D: Super Chargers

4

In a 2006 World Cup quarter-final penalty shoot-out, who saved a penalty from Frank Lampard?

- A: Mark Schwarzer
- B: Ricardo
- C: Edwin van der Sar
- D: Kasey Keller

If you would like to use your 50:50 please turn to page 293
If you would like to use your Ask The Audience please turn to page 316
Turn to the answer section on page 330 to find out if you've won £300!

3 ◆ £300 WORLD CUP

5

In October 2009, what was thrown on to the pitch during the Ukraine v England game?

- A: Rugby ball
- B: Lit flares
- C: Inflatable doll
- D: Rubber chicken

6

What was banned at the 1986 tournament?

- A: Goal celebrations
- B: Shirt swapping
- C: Cheering
- D: Substitutions

7

Who did Clarence Seedorf, Patrick Kluivert and Edwin van der Sar play World Cup football for?

- A: Belgium
- B: Germany
- C: France
- D: The Netherlands

8

Which of these teams did not qualify for the 2010 finals from the South American confederation?

- A: Paraguay
- B: Chile
- C: Honduras
- D: Brazil

If you would like to use your 50:50 please turn to page 293
If you would like to use your Ask The Audience please turn to page 316
Turn to the answer section on page 330 to find out if you've won £300!

3 ◆ £300 WORLD CUP

9

Which team from Oceania qualified for 2010?

- A: South Korea
- B: North Korea
- C: Japan
- D: New Zealand

10

At the 2006 World Cup, what colour were Croatia's first-choice shirts?

- A: Red and white check
- B: Blue and white stripe
- C: Yellow and white hoop
- D: All white

11

Which 2010 qualifying team is nicknamed 'Equipo Azteca' or 'El Tri'?

- A: Brazil
- B: Mexico
- C: Portugal
- D: Spain

12

Which of these 2010 qualifying teams is nicknamed 'La Roja', meaning 'The Red One'?

- A: France
- B: Côte d'Ivoire
- C: Chile
- D: Italy

If you would like to use your 50:50 please turn to page 293
If you would like to use your Ask The Audience please turn to page 316
Turn to the answer section on page 330 to find out if you've won £300!

3 ◆ £300 WORLD CUP

13

Which 2010 qualifying team is sometimes nicknamed 'Little Canary'?

- A: Serbia
- B: The Netherlands
- C: Côte d'Ivoire
- D: Brazil

14

Who did not lose a World Cup match until the semi-final of the 1954 tournament?

- A: England
- B: Scotland
- C: Uruguay
- D: Bolivia

15

Which was the only South American country to compete at the 1938 World Cup?

- A: Bolivia
- B: Colombia
- C: Brazil
- D: Venezuela

16

Who are the only World Cup champions not to defend their title?

- A: Brazil
- B: England
- C: France
- D: Uruguay

If you would like to use your 50:50 please turn to page 293
If you would like to use your Ask The Audience please turn to page 316
Turn to the answer section on page 330 to find out if you've won £300!

3 ◆ £300 WORLD CUP

17

Which 1930 World Cup squad was selected by HRH King Carol?

- A: France
- B: Argentina
- C: Romania
- D: Bolivia

18

Which country hosted the very first World Cup tournament in 1930?

- A: England
- B: Romania
- C: Belgium
- D: Uruguay

19

Geographically and population-wise, which was the smallest country to qualify for South Africa?

- A: Slovenia
- B: Algeria
- C: Australia
- D: Argentina

20

Which team has reached the finals of the World Cup more times than the others put together?

- A: Ghana
- B: New Zealand
- C: Côte d'Ivoire
- D: Spain

If you would like to use your 50:50 please turn to page 293
If you would like to use your Ask The Audience please turn to page 316
Turn to the answer section on page 330 to find out if you've won £300!

3 ◆ £300 WORLD CUP

21

Which of the following was one of England's heroes at the 1990 tournament?

- A: Terry Butcher
- B: Terry Baker
- C: Terry Tinker
- D: Terry Sailor

22

What colour shirts did England wear in the final match of their 1966 triumph?

- A: Red
- B: Blue
- C: Green
- D: Black

23

What was the name of the USA coach at the 2006 finals?

- A: Chad Stadium
- B: Troy Executive-Box
- C: Brett Goalpost
- D: Bruce Arena

24

Which of these teams was not drawn in England's first-round group for the 2006 finals?

- A: Paraguay
- B: Sweden
- C: Trinidad & Tobago
- D: Germany

If you would like to use your 50:50 please turn to page 293
If you would like to use your Ask The Audience please turn to page 316
Turn to the answer section on page 330 to find out if you've won £300!

3 ◆ £300 WORLD CUP

25

Michael Owen broke a bone in which part of his body prior to the 2006 World Cup finals?

- A: Arm
- B: Hand
- C: Nose
- D: Foot

26

Which side did Martin O'Neill captain at the 1982 tournament?

- A: Northern Ireland
- B: Italy
- C: West Germany
- D: Austria

27

Which country were seeded highest when the draw was made for the 2006 World Cup finals?

- A: Uruguay
- B: South Korea
- C: Paraguay
- D: Brazil

28

Where did Sol Campbell play for England in 1998 and 2002?

- A: Goalkeeper
- B: Defence
- C: Midfield
- D: Attack

If you would like to use your 50:50 please turn to page 293
If you would like to use your Ask The Audience please turn to page 316
Turn to the answer section on page 330 to find out if you've won £300!

3 ◆ £300 WORLD CUP

29

The present World Cup trophy is chiefly made from which material?

- A: Glass
- B: Gold
- C: Tin
- D: Copper

30

What role was played by Pierluigi Collina in the 2002 World Cup final?

- A: Winning captain
- B: Referee
- C: Streaker
- D: Scored winner

31

The current World Cup trophy is a representation of two figures supporting what?

- A: Football
- B: Sun
- C: Globe
- D: Football boot

32

The ball used in the 2006 World Cup final featured which colour?

- A: Purple
- B: Gold
- C: Pink
- D: Green

If you would like to use your 50:50 please turn to page 293
If you would like to use your Ask The Audience please turn to page 316
Turn to the answer section on pages 330–331 to find out if you've won £300!

3 ◆ £300 WORLD CUP

33

At the World Cup finals, the first-round groups are identified by what?

- A: Colours
- B: Letters
- C: Animals
- D: Footballers

34

Which team was captained by Michel Platini at the 1982 and 1986 World Cup finals?

- A: Italy
- B: Argentina
- C: France
- D: Switzerland

35

The 1966 World Cup winner Jack Charlton later managed which World Cup team?

- A: France
- B: England
- C: Republic of Ireland
- D: Saudi Arabia

36

Luís Figo, Rui Costa and Maniche played World Cup football for which team?

- A: Brazil
- B: Spain
- C: Portugal
- D: Argentina

If you would like to use your 50:50 please turn to page 293
If you would like to use your Ask The Audience please turn to page 316
Turn to the answer section on page 331 to find out if you've won £300!

3 ◆ £300 WORLD CUP

37

Who said 'Some people think I haven't got the brains to be that clever' after a 2006 qualifier?

- A: David Beckham
- B: Rio Ferdinand
- C: Michael Owen
- D: Wayne Rooney

38

For which 2006 qualifier did Freddie Ljungberg play?

- A: England
- B: France
- C: Italy
- D: Sweden

39

At what stage were England eliminated from the 2002 tournament?

- A: Semi-final
- B: Quarter-final
- C: First round
- D: Second round

40

Major League Soccer is the domestic league of which 2010 qualifier?

- A: England
- B: France
- C: Italy
- D: USA

If you would like to use your 50:50 please turn to page 293
If you would like to use your Ask The Audience please turn to page 316
Turn to the answer section on page 331 to find out if you've won £300!

3 ◆ £300 WORLD CUP

41

Who shaved off all his hair apart from a wedge-shaped patch at the front for the 2002 final?

- A: David Seaman
- B: Ronaldo
- C: Rio Ferdinand
- D: David Beckham

42

Billy Bremner, Kenny Dalglish and Denis Law played World Cup football for which team?

- A: Denmark
- B: Belgium
- C: Scotland
- D: USA

43

Which of these teams did not reach the semi-finals of the 2006 tournament?

- A: Germany
- B: Portugal
- C: Italy
- D: Brazil

44

Which of these teams did not qualify for the 2010 finals from the Asian confederation?

- A: New Zealand
- B: Japan
- C: North Korea
- D: South Korea

If you would like to use your 50:50 please turn to page 293
If you would like to use your Ask The Audience please turn to page 316
Turn to the answer section on page 331 to find out if you've won £300!

3 ◆ £300 WORLD CUP

45

In which Italian city was the final of the 1934 World Cup played?

- A: Milan
- B: Naples
- C: Florence
- D: Rome

46

Who coached Brazil to their 2002 triumph?

- A: Terry Venables
- B: Guus Hiddink
- C: Jack Charlton
- D: Felipe Scolari

47

Which of these teams has never qualified for the World Cup finals?

- A: Sweden
- B: Denmark
- C: Norway
- D: Faroe Islands

48

Park Ji-Sung played for which country in their 2010 campaign?

- A: Japan
- B: New Zealand
- C: Cameroon
- D: South Korea

If you would like to use your 50:50 please turn to page 293
If you would like to use your Ask The Audience please turn to page 316
Turn to the answer section on page 331 to find out if you've won £300!

49

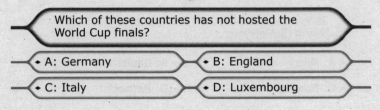

Which of these countries has not hosted the World Cup finals?

- A: Germany
- B: England
- C: Italy
- D: Luxembourg

If you would like to use your 50:50 please turn to page 293
If you would like to use your Ask The Audience please turn to page 316
Turn to the answer section on page 331 to find out if you've won £300!

3 ◆ £300 EUROPEAN

1

Who did not qualify from the group stages of the 2009/10 Champions League?

- A: Real Madrid
- B: Chelsea
- C: Barcelona
- D: Debrecen

2

In the Intercontinental Cup, teams from Europe would play against teams from where?

- A: Africa
- B: Australia
- C: South America
- D: Asia

3

The Europa League replaced which other tournament?

- A: UEFA Cup
- B: Cup Winners' Cup
- C: European Super Cup
- D: Champions League

4

By what general name is the top flight of Spanish domestic football known?

- A: Serie A
- B: Bundesliga
- C: Ligue 1
- D: La Liga

If you would like to use your 50:50 please turn to page 293
If you would like to use your Ask The Audience please turn to page 316
Turn to the answer section on page 331 to find out if you've won £300!

3 ◆ £300 EUROPEAN

5

Andoni Zubizarreta is which country's most capped player?

- A: Latvia
- B: Iceland
- C: Spain
- D: Germany

6

Which former Manchester United player returned to play against them in the 2009/10 Champions League?

- A: Roy Carroll
- B: David Beckham
- C: Phil Neville
- D: Dwight Yorke

7

Sparta Rotterdam is the oldest professional football club in which country?

- A: Portugal
- B: Poland
- C: Slovakia
- D: The Netherlands

8

Which of these stadia is in Madrid?

- A: Allianz Arena
- B: Parc des Princes
- C: Wembley
- D: Bernabéu

If you would like to use your 50:50 please turn to page 293
If you would like to use your Ask The Audience please turn to page 316
Turn to the answer section on page 331 to find out if you've won £300!

3 ◆ £300 EUROPEAN

9

Sparta, Slavia and Bohemians are clubs based in which capital city?

- A: Berlin
- B: Brussels
- C: Prague
- D: Paris

10

MTK, Honved and Ferencváros are teams based in which city?

- A: Berlin
- B: Barcelona
- C: Bonn
- D: Budapest

11

Which of these clubs would normally wear striped shirts?

- A: Manchester United
- B: Real Madrid
- C: Juventus
- D: Bayern Munich

12

What is the predominant colour of Real Madrid's first-choice strip?

- A: All red
- B: All green
- C: All black
- D: All white

If you would like to use your 50:50 please turn to page 293
If you would like to use your Ask The Audience please turn to page 316
Turn to the answer section on page 331 to find out if you've won £300!

3 ◆ £300 EUROPEAN

13

What follows Zenit to give the name of a top Russian club?

- A: Kazan
- B: Moscow
- C: St Petersburg
- D: Volgograd

14

For which country did the female star Bente Nordby play international football?

- A: Germany
- B: Norway
- C: Nigeria
- D: China

15

What is the name of Germany's premier domestic league?

- A: Serie A
- B: Premier League
- C: La Liga
- D: Bundesliga

16

Which of these would not be an international game between neighbouring countries?

- A: Spain v Portugal
- B: France v Russia
- C: England v Scotland
- D: Norway v Sweden

If you would like to use your 50:50 please turn to pages 293–294
If you would like to use your Ask The Audience please turn to page 316–317
Turn to the answer section on page 331 to find out if you've won £300!

3 ◆ £300 EUROPEAN

17

Which of these clubs is based on the Iberian peninsula?

- A: Benfica
- B: Galatasaray
- C: Rangers
- D: Anderlecht

18

Which European country wears red and white checked shirts?

- A: Croatia
- B: Scotland
- C: Sweden
- D: Poland

19

Which of these are two teams from the same city?

- A: Lazio and Parma
- B: Lyon and Auxerre
- C: Hamburg and Schalke 04
- D: Barcelona and Espanyol

20

As of January 2010, Raúl is the top goalscorer for which country?

- A: Spain
- B: Greece
- C: Austria
- D: France

If you would like to use your 50:50 please turn to page 294
If you would like to use your Ask The Audience please turn to page 317
Turn to the answer section on page 331 to find out if you've won £300!

3 ◆ £300 EUROPEAN

21

Which national team are known as the 'Oranje'?

- A: Sweden
- B: Germany
- C: The Netherlands
- D: Poland

22

Green is the favoured colour for which country's shirts?

- A: Republic of Ireland
- B: Greece
- C: Turkey
- D: Switzerland

23

What follows Rapid, Dynamo and Steaua to make the names of three football clubs?

- A: Bonn
- B: Bratislava
- C: Barcelona
- D: Bucharest

24

Which of these would Cristiano Ronaldo hear before playing for his country?

- A: 'God Save the Queen'
- B: 'La Marseillaise'
- C: 'A Portuguesa'
- D: 'Het Wilhelmus'

If you would like to use your 50:50 please turn to page 294
If you would like to use your Ask The Audience please turn to page 317
Turn to the answer section on page 331 to find out if you've won £300!

3 ◆ £300 DOMESTIC

1

Beau Brummie is the mascot of which club?

- A: Newcastle United
- B: Manchester United
- C: Bolton Wanderers
- D: Birmingham City

2

In the 2009/10 season, who sponsored the Conference Premier League?

- A: Green Pentagon
- B: Red Trapezium
- C: Blue Square
- D: Yellow Rhombus

3

Which of these teams did Brian Clough not manage?

- A: Leeds United
- B: Sheffield United
- C: Derby County
- D: Nottingham Forest

4

Besides Derby County, which is the only other league club in Derbyshire?

- A: Rotherham United
- B: Port Vale
- C: Grimsby Town
- D: Chesterfield

If you would like to use your 50:50 please turn to page 294
If you would like to use your Ask The Audience please turn to page 317
Turn to the answer section on page 331 to find out if you've won £300!

3 ◆ £300 DOMESTIC

5

Which club's home ground is situated on land once owned by the sixth Baron Craven?

- A: Millwall
- B: Crystal Palace
- C: Chelsea
- D: Fulham

6

Complete the title of the song which has become synonymous with Bristol Rovers 'Goodnight . . .'

- A: Maureen
- B: Colleen
- C: Irene
- D: Mabeline

7

In which city are the grounds of two league clubs within two minutes walking distance?

- A: Southampton
- B: Norwich
- C: Dundee
- D: Sunderland

8

In 1993, who became the first-ever winners of the Premier League?

- A: Sunderland
- B: Ipswich Town
- C: Manchester United
- D: Aston Villa

If you would like to use your 50:50 please turn to page 294
If you would like to use your Ask The Audience please turn to page 317
Turn to the answer section on page 331 to find out if you've won £300!

3 ◆ £300 DOMESTIC

9

As of 2009, which club has not won the Premiership more than once?

- A: Arsenal
- B: Manchester United
- C: Blackburn Rovers
- D: Chelsea

10

Which club reached the Championship in 2006, fourteen years after being Conference champions?

- A: Yeovil Town
- B: Colchester United
- C: Accrington Stanley
- D: Lincoln City

11

Which of these has not been a name of the League Cup?

- A: Rumbelows Cup
- B: Worthington Cup
- C: British Telecom Cup
- D: Carling Cup

12

Which club operates a 'Valley Express' bus service to bring fans from out of London to matches?

- A: Chelsea
- B: QPR
- C: Millwall
- D: Charlton Athletic

If you would like to use your 50:50 please turn to page 294
If you would like to use your Ask The Audience please turn to page 317
Turn to the answer section on page 331 to find out if you've won £300!

3 ◆ £300 DOMESTIC

13

At what stage of the FA Cup do the Premier League teams enter the competition?

- A: 3rd round
- B: 4th round
- C: 5th round
- D: 6th round

14

Which England goalkeeper sported a ponytail towards the end of his career?

- A: Peter Shilton
- B: David Seaman
- C: Ray Clemence
- D: Gordon Banks

15

Which of these is a Northern Irish league club?

- A: Glencampbell
- B: Glenmcgrath
- C: Glennhoddle
- D: Glentoran

16

Which sportswear company supplied England with their team shirts prior to 1984?

- A: Brigadier
- B: General
- C: Admiral
- D: Commodore

If you would like to use your 50:50 please turn to page 294
If you would like to use your Ask The Audience please turn to page 317
Turn to the answer section on page 331 to find out if you've won £300!

3 ◆ £300 DOMESTIC

17

As of the 2009/2010 season, which is the only 'United' in the Scottish Premier League?

- A: Aberdeen
- B: Kilmarnock
- C: Dundee
- D: Motherwell

18

Historically, on what day were local derby matches commonly played?

- A: Christmas Eve
- B: Christmas Day
- C: Boxing Day
- D: New Year's Eve

19

Which Kenny won eighty-six caps for England?

- A: Dalglish
- B: Rogers
- C: Sansom
- D: Lynch

20

Which England defender captained his country in the 1980s?

- A: Terry Baker
- B: Terry Barber
- C: Terry Butcher
- D: Terry Banker

If you would like to use your 50:50 please turn to page 294
If you would like to use your Ask The Audience please turn to page 317
Turn to the answer section on page 331 to find out if you've won £300!

3 ◆ £300 DOMESTIC

21

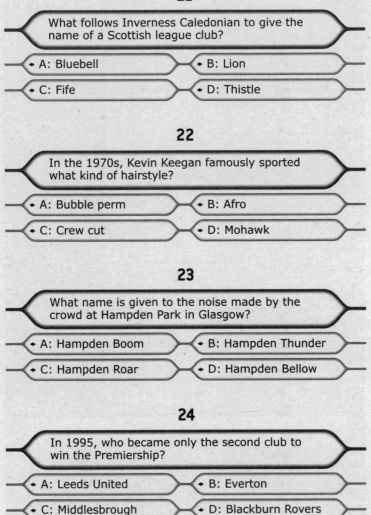

What follows Inverness Caledonian to give the name of a Scottish league club?

- A: Bluebell
- B: Lion
- C: Fife
- D: Thistle

22

In the 1970s, Kevin Keegan famously sported what kind of hairstyle?

- A: Bubble perm
- B: Afro
- C: Crew cut
- D: Mohawk

23

What name is given to the noise made by the crowd at Hampden Park in Glasgow?

- A: Hampden Boom
- B: Hampden Thunder
- C: Hampden Roar
- D: Hampden Bellow

24

In 1995, who became only the second club to win the Premiership?

- A: Leeds United
- B: Everton
- C: Middlesbrough
- D: Blackburn Rovers

If you would like to use your 50:50 please turn to page 294
If you would like to use your Ask The Audience please turn to page 317
Turn to the answer section on page 331 to find out if you've won £300!

50:50

15	£1 MILLION
14	£5000,00
13	£250,000
12	£125,000
11	£64,000
10	£32,000
9	£16,000
8	£8,000
7	£4,000
6	£2,000
5	£1,000
4	£500
3	£300
2	£200
1	£100

4 ◆ £500 WORLD CUP

1

At the time of the 1930 World Cup, which team were Olympic football champions?

- A: Panama
- B: Uruguay
- C: Romania
- D: Mexico

2

Prior to 2010, which team has reached the final of the World Cup twice but lost each time?

- A: Argentina
- B: Germany
- C: The Netherlands
- D: Italy

3

Which 2010 qualifiers are nicknamed 'La Celeste Olímpica', meaning 'The Olympic Sky Blue'?

- A: Argentina
- B: Portugal
- C: Uruguay
- D: France

4

How were the eight groups identified at the 2010 World Cup finals?

- A: One to eight
- B: A to H
- C: Alpha to theta
- D: I to VIII

If you would like to use your 50:50 please turn to page 295
If you would like to use your Ask The Audience please turn to page 317
Turn to the answer section on page 331 to find out if you've won £500!

4 ◆ £500 WORLD CUP

5

In 2002, which became the first Asian Confederation team to reach a World Cup semi-final?

- A: Yemen
- B: China
- C: Iran
- D: South Korea

6

What was the final score in England's victory in the 1966 World Cup final?

- A: 5-1
- B: 4-2
- C: 3-0
- D: 7-6

7

Who coached Italy to their fourth World Cup Crown in 2006?

- A: Franco Verdi
- B: Giuseppe Nero
- C: Stefano Rossi
- D: Marcello Lippi

8

Which of Germany's neighbours has yet to appear in the World Cup finals?

- A: Luxembourg
- B: Belgium
- C: France
- D: Poland

If you would like to use your 50:50 please turn to page 295
If you would like to use your Ask The Audience please turn to page 317
Turn to the answer section on page 331 to find out if you've won £500!

4 ◆ £500 WORLD CUP

9

By what name was the World Cup trophy known when England won it in 1966?

- A: Pompidou Cup
- B: Edith Piaf Plate
- C: Jules Rimet Trophy
- D: Stella Artois Cup

10

Whose version of 'Nessun Dorma' was the BBC's theme song for the 1990 World Cup?

- A: José Carreras
- B: Placido Domingo
- C: Zubin Mehta
- D: Luciano Pavarotti

11

The World Cup finals have never been staged on which of these continents?

- A: North America
- B: Asia
- C: Australia
- D: South America

12

Who famously cried when yellow-carded in a 1990 World Cup semi-final?

- A: Paul Gascoigne
- B: John Barnes
- C: Bryan Robson
- D: David Platt

If you would like to use your 50:50 please turn to page 295
If you would like to use your Ask The Audience please turn to page 317
Turn to the answer section on page 331 to find out if you've won £500!

4 ◆ £500 WORLD CUP

13

Which of these future England managers was part of the 1982 England World Cup finals squad?

- A: Bobby Robson
- B: Steve McLaren
- C: Kevin Keegan
- D: Peter Taylor

14

Which was the only country that entered a bid to host the 2014 World Cup finals?

- A: Brazil
- B: Botswana
- C: Burundi
- D: Bhutan

15

As of 2010, which country's only qualification for the World Cup finals was in 1986?

- A: Canada
- B: Spain
- C: Mexico
- D: France

16

Which country hosted the World Cup finals twice within the space of sixteen years?

- A: England
- B: Japan
- C: USA
- D: Mexico

If you would like to use your 50:50 please turn to page 295
If you would like to use your Ask The Audience please turn to page 317
Turn to the answer section on page 331 to find out if you've won £500!

4 ◆ £500 WORLD CUP

17

Which country lost all ten of its 2010 World Cup qualifying games?

- A: Andorra
- B: England
- C: Italy
- D: Germany

18

Which country won all ten of its 2010 World Cup qualifying games?

- A: Andorra
- B: San Marino
- C: Liechtenstein
- D: Spain

19

Which country that has been playing since 1993 reached the 2010 World Cup finals?

- A: Slovakia
- B: Vanuatu
- C: Antigua
- D: Yemen

20

The award for the top scorer at the World Cup finals is correctly known as the Adidas . . .?

- A: Golden Ball
- B: Golden Shoe
- C: Golden Stud
- D: Golden Laces

If you would like to use your 50:50 please turn to page 295
If you would like to use your Ask The Audience please turn to page 317
Turn to the answer section on page 331 to find out if you've won £500!

4 ◆ £500 WORLD CUP

21

Which of these men did not manage the England team at the World Cup finals?

- A: Glenn Hoddle
- B: Joe Mercer
- C: Bobby Robson
- D: Alf Ramsey

22

What made the 2002 World Cup different from any previous World Cups?

- A: All night games
- B: No yellow cards
- C: Played in winter
- D: Joint hosts

23

Which of these players never lifted the World Cup trophy?

- A: Cafu
- B: Diego Maradona
- C: Bobby Moore
- D: George Best

24

In the first round of the World Cup finals, the teams are divided into groups of how many?

- A: Four
- B: Six
- C: Eight
- D: Sixteen

If you would like to use your 50:50 please turn to page 295
If you would like to use your Ask The Audience please turn to page 317
Turn to the answer section on page 331 to find out if you've won £500!

4 ◆ £500 WORLD CUP

25

Who played for England in 1982 and 1986, and managed them at the 1998 World Cup finals?

- A: John Barnes
- B: Glenn Hoddle
- C: Bryan Robson
- D: Stuart Pearce

26

For which team did Rivaldo score five goals in the 2002 World Cup finals?

- A: Portugal
- B: Turkey
- C: Paraguay
- D: Brazil

27

Who was dubbed 'Turnip Head' by the media, after failing to take England to the World Cup?

- A: Kevin Keegan
- B: Terry Venables
- C: Glenn Hoddle
- D: Graham Taylor

28

Who was not named as a goalkeeper in the England 2006 World Cup squad?

- A: Paul Robinson
- B: Scott Carson
- C: David James
- D: Jermaine Jenas

If you would like to use your 50:50 please turn to page 295
If you would like to use your Ask The Audience please turn to page 317
Turn to the answer section on page 331 to find out if you've won £500!

4 ◆ £500 WORLD CUP

29

The team of which 2006 qualifier was formed only after the break-up of the Soviet Union?

- A: Angola
- B: South Korea
- C: Ukraine
- D: Japan

30

What is the maximum number of substitutes a team may use during a World Cup match?

- A: Three
- B: Five
- C: Seven
- D: Nine

31

Which South American nation made its debut at the World Cup finals in 2002?

- A: Uruguay
- B: Brazil
- C: Argentina
- D: Ecuador

32

Which of these teams did not reach the quarter-finals of the 2006 tournament?

- A: Argentina
- B: Ukraine
- C: England
- D: Sweden

If you would like to use your 50:50 please turn to page 295
If you would like to use your Ask The Audience please turn to page 317
Turn to the answer section on page 331 to find out if you've won £500!

4 ◆ £500 WORLD CUP

33

Which country hosted the first World Cup to be held in Europe after World War II?

- A: The Netherlands
- B: Belgium
- C: Germany
- D: Switzerland

34

Players in which World Cup-winning team are often known by a single name?

- A: Germany
- B: Brazil
- C: England
- D: Italy

35

Which of these countries did not take part in the qualifying rounds of the 2010 World Cup?

- A: Brunei
- B: Bolivia
- C: Belgium
- D: Brazil

36

A venue for the 2010 tournament, the stadium in Port Elizabeth is named after whom?

- A: P.W. Botha
- B: F.W. De Klerk
- C: Nelson Mandela
- D: Thabo Mbeki

If you would like to use your 50:50 please turn to page 295
If you would like to use your Ask The Audience please turn to page 317–318
Turn to the answer section on page 331 to find out if you've won £500!

4 ◆ £500 WORLD CUP

37

Los Charrúas is the nickname of which 2010 World Cup finals team?

- A: Greece
- B: Denmark
- C: USA
- D: Uruguay

38

Which was the highest-ranked team drawn in Group D for the 2010 World Cup finals?

- A: Ghana
- B: Serbia
- C: Germany
- D: Australia

39

Which was the highest-ranked team drawn in Group B for the 2010 World Cup finals?

- A: Greece
- B: South Korea
- C: Nigeria
- D: Argentina

40

For which club was Bobby Charlton playing when he won his 1966 World Cup medal?

- A: Newcastle United
- B: Preston North End
- C: Chelsea
- D: Manchester United

If you would like to use your 50:50 please turn to page 295
If you would like to use your Ask The Audience please turn to page 318
Turn to the answer section on page 331 to find out if you've won £500!

4 ◆ £500 WORLD CUP

41

Which of these countries has never won the World Cup?

- A: England
- B: Italy
- C: Brazil
- D: Spain

42

Prior to 2010, which of these teams has Germany not defeated in a World Cup final?

- A: Hungary
- B: The Netherlands
- C: England
- D: Argentina

43

Which country is abbreviated on the World Cup website as MLI?

- A: Malawi
- B: Morocco
- C: Mauritania
- D: Mali

44

By what nickname is the New Zealand national football team known?

- A: All Blacks
- B: Silver Ferns
- C: White Feathers
- D: All Whites

If you would like to use your 50:50 please turn to page 295
If you would like to use your Ask The Audience please turn to page 318
Turn to the answer section on page 331 to find out if you've won £500!

4 ◆ £500 WORLD CUP

45

Which of these former countries never appeared in the World Cup finals?

- A: Soviet Union
- B: Czechoslovakia
- C: East Germany
- D: South Vietnam

46

Which team won the 2002 World Cup?

- A: Italy
- B: Germany
- C: Brazil
- D: France

47

Gary Lineker described football as a game 'played for 120 minutes and then the . . .'?

- A: Germans win
- B: Fat lady sings
- C: Lights go out
- D: Ref blows up

If you would like to use your 50:50 please turn to page 295
If you would like to use your Ask The Audience please turn to page 318
Turn to the answer section on page 331 to find out if you've won £500!

4 ◆ £500 EUROPEAN

1

Which of these is the home ground of the Bundesliga team VfL Wolfsburg?

- A: Ford Stadium
- B: Volkswagen Arena
- C: Toyota Park
- D: Lancia Campus

2

Which of these is a top Czech team?

- A: Sparta Paris
- B: Sparta Plymouth
- C: Sparta Palermo
- D: Sparta Prague

3

In which year were the finals of the European Championship hosted by England?

- A: 1992
- B: 1996
- C: 2000
- D: 2004

4

Which of these is a top-flight Norwegian club?

- A: Visigoth FK
- B: Vandal FK
- C: Viking FK
- D: Varlet FK

If you would like to use your 50:50 please turn to page 295
If you would like to use your Ask The Audience please turn to page 318
Turn to the answer section on page 331 to find out if you've won £500!

5

How does the nickname of Benfica's home ground, Estadio da Luz, translate into English?

- A: Eusébio Park
- B: Lucozade Stadium
- C: Benfica Boulevard
- D: Stadium of Light

6

In which city would a local derby between Austria Wien and Rapid Wien take place?

- A: Salzburg
- B: Innsbruck
- C: Linz
- D: Vienna

7

What Spanish term is used to describe an expensive, world-famous player?

- A: Superbo
- B: Galáctico
- C: Prodigalo
- D: Primo

8

Which national team is nicknamed 'Les Bleus'?

- A: Albania
- B: Republic of Ireland
- C: Germany
- D: France

If you would like to use your 50:50 please turn to page 295
If you would like to use your Ask The Audience please turn to page 318
Turn to the answer section on page 331 to find out if you've won £500!

4 ◆ £500 EUROPEAN

9

What does the 'U' stand for in the acronym UEFA?

- A: Union
- B: Unison
- C: United
- D: Unification

10

Which Scottish club reached the group stages of the 2009/10 Champions League?

- A: Rangers
- B: Raith Rovers
- C: Morton
- D: Montrose

11

Which country did not have a team in the group stages of the 2009/10 Champions League?

- A: Switzerland
- B: France
- C: Wales
- D: Turkey

12

Which of these countries does not have a national football league?

- A: Greece
- B: Norway
- C: Portugal
- D: Liechtenstein

If you would like to use your 50:50 please turn to page 295
If you would like to use your Ask The Audience please turn to page 318
Turn to the answer section on pages 331–332 to find out if you've won £500!

4 ◆ £500 EUROPEAN

13

As of January 2010, which country has yet to win a competitive international match?

- A: Finland
- B: Denmark
- C: Belgium
- D: San Marino

14

In which country was Sven-Göran Eriksson born?

- A: Germany
- B: France
- C: Sweden
- D: Spain

15

Where do the clubs 07 Vestur, B68 Toftir and HB Tórshavn play their home matches?

- A: Scotland
- B: Faroe Islands
- C: Wales
- D: Northern Ireland

16

By what name is the famous Stadio Giuseppe Meazza in Milan familiarly known?

- A: Stadio del Luz
- B: Parco d'Italia
- C: San Siro
- D: Giardino Milano

If you would like to use your 50:50 please turn to page 295
If you would like to use your Ask The Audience please turn to page 318
Turn to the answer section on page 332 to find out if you've won £500!

4 ◆ £500 EUROPEAN

17

By what name is football known in Italy?

- A: Calcio
- B: Prosciutto
- C: Raddichio
- D: Zucchero

18

In which European capital city does Lazio play its home matches?

- A: Rome
- B: Prague
- C: Berlin
- D: Paris

19

Which of these is not a Turkish club?

- A: Fenerbahçe
- B: Panathinaikos
- C: Galatasaray
- D: Besiktas

20

Which country has yet to produce a Champions League-winning team?

- A: Spain
- B: England
- C: Germany
- D: Wales

If you would like to use your 50:50 please turn to pages 295–296
If you would like to use your Ask The Audience please turn to page 318
Turn to the answer section on page 332 to find out if you've won £500!

4 ◆ £500 EUROPEAN

21

What is a Europass Gloria, as used in the final of Euro 2008?

- A: Match ball
- B: Referee's whistle
- C: Corner flag
- D: Countdown clock

22

What was the motto of Euro 2008?

- A: Expect goals
- B: Expect fire
- C: Expect the best
- D: Expect emotions

23

The Hellenic Football Federation is the association for which country?

- A: Switzerland
- B: Norway
- C: Denmark
- D: Greece

If you would like to use your 50:50 please turn to page 296
If you would like to use your Ask The Audience please turn to page 318
Turn to the answer section on page 332 to find out if you've won £500!

4 ◆ £500 DOMESTIC

1

Which was the most southerly club playing in the 2009/10 Premier League?

- A: Reading
- B: Chelsea
- C: Fulham
- D: Portsmouth

2

Which club shares its name with the venue of the Great Exhibition of 1851?

- A: Port Vale
- B: Crystal Palace
- C: Aston Villa
- D: Millwall

3

What nickname links Liverpool and Nottingham Forest?

- A: The Blues
- B: The Reds
- C: The Whites
- D: The Golds

4

Which former England manager died in July 2009?

- A: Ron Greenwood
- B: Joe Mercer
- C: Bobby Robson
- D: Graham Taylor

If you would like to use your 50:50 please turn to page 296
If you would like to use your Ask The Audience please turn to page 318
Turn to the answer section on page 332 to find out if you've won £500!

4 ◆ £500 DOMESTIC

5

About which fish did Eric Cantona make a famous quote?

- A: Pilchards
- B: Mackerel
- C: Trout
- D: Sardines

6

The Shed End is a feature of which ground?

- A: Old Trafford
- B: Stamford Bridge
- C: White Hart Lane
- D: Goodison Park

7

Which club's traditional colours are claret and light blue?

- A: Arsenal
- B: Aston Villa
- C: Newcastle United
- D: Liverpool

8

The TV documentary 'Old Big 'Ead' was a tribute to which manager?

- A: Alex Ferguson
- B: Bob Paisley
- C: Brian Clough
- D: Alf Ramsey

If you would like to use your 50:50 please turn to page 296
If you would like to use your Ask The Audience please turn to page 318
Turn to the answer section on page 332 to find out if you've won £500!

4 ◆ £500 DOMESTIC

9

Which of these players has not been signed to an overseas club while on England duty?

- A: David Beckham
- B: Steven Gerrard
- C: Gary Lineker
- D: Mark Hateley

10

Which club is nicknamed after a farm animal?

- A: Sheffield United
- B: Middlesbrough
- C: Wigan Athletic
- D: Derby County

11

The Premier League season usually finishes in which month?

- A: April
- B: May
- C: June
- D: July

12

Who stood down as Birmingham City's chairman in 2009?

- A: Billy Brass
- B: Sam Silver
- C: Tim Tin
- D: David Gold

If you would like to use your 50:50 please turn to page 296
If you would like to use your Ask The Audience please turn to page 318
Turn to the answer section on page 332 to find out if you've won £500!

4 ◆ £500 DOMESTIC

13

Who plays home games at Portman Road?

- A: Hull City
- B: Ipswich Town
- C: Leicester City
- D: Leyton Orient

14

With 206 goals, who is Newcastle United's all-time leading scorer?

- A: Kevin Keegan
- B: Alan Shearer
- C: Malcolm Macdonald
- D: Jackie Milburn

15

What is the affectionate nickname of the manager Sam Allardyce?

- A: Little Sam
- B: Big Sam
- C: Fat Sam
- D: Uncle Sam

16

What insects appear on the badge of Brentford?

- A: Cockroaches
- B: Ants
- C: Bees
- D: Beetles

If you would like to use your 50:50 please turn to page 296
If you would like to use your Ask The Audience please turn to page 318
Turn to the answer section on page 332 to find out if you've won £500!

4 ◆ £500 DOMESTIC

17

Which of these 2009/10 Chelsea players is a German international?

- A: Didier Drogba
- B: Nicolas Anelka
- C: Deco
- D: Michael Ballack

18

Complete the title of Sir Alex Ferguson's autobiography, *Managing . . .*

- A: *My Life*
- B: *My Temper*
- C: *My Team*
- D: *My Glory*

19

Complete the name of the 2009/10 Manchester City player, Shaun Wright-. . .

- A: Phillips
- B: Johns
- C: James
- D: Toms

20

How many years as Arsenal's manager did Arsène Wenger celebrate in October 2009?

- A: Three
- B: Five
- C: Seven
- D: Thirteen

If you would like to use your 50:50 please turn to page 296
If you would like to use your Ask The Audience please turn to page 318
Turn to the answer section on page 332 to find out if you've won £500!

4 ◆ £500 DOMESTIC

21

While playing for which of these clubs did Kevin Keegan not win an England cap?

- A: Hamburg
- B: Liverpool
- C: Southampton
- D: Scunthorpe United

22

The semi-finals for which of these are played over two legs?

- A: English FA Cup
- B: Scottish FA Cup
- C: Football League Cup
- D: Scottish League Cup

23

Who is the 2009/10 Manchester United and England player?

- A: Wes Green
- B: Wes White
- C: Wes Black
- D: Wes Brown

If you would like to use your 50:50 please turn to page 296
If you would like to use your Ask The Audience please turn to page 318
Turn to the answer section on page 332 to find out if you've won £500!

50:50

15	£1 MILLION
14	£5000,00
13	£250,000
12	£125,000
11	£64,000
10	£32,000
9	£16,000
8	£8,000
7	£4,000
6	£2,000
5	£1,000
4	£500
3	£300
2	£200
1	£100

5 ◆ £1000 WORLD CUP

1

Which French World Cup hero was nicknamed 'Zizou'?

- A: Michel Platini
- B: Jean Tigana
- C: Thierry Henry
- D: Zinedine Zidane

2

In which year did Scotland last qualify for the World Cup finals?

- A: 2002
- B: 1998
- C: 1994
- D: 1990

3

Which of these former champions failed to progress past the first round in 2002?

- A: England
- B: Germany
- C: Argentina
- D: Brazil

4

Who is the only English player to have won the Golden Shoe award?

- A: Michael Owen
- B: Gary Lineker
- C: Kevin Keegan
- D: Geoff Hurst

If you would like to use your 50:50 please turn to page 297
If you would like to use your Ask The Audience please turn to page 318
Turn to the answer section on page 332 to find out if you've won £1000!

5 ◆ £1000 WORLD CUP

5

Which opponents did Brazil overcome in the final of both the 1970 and 1994 tournaments?

- A: Italy
- B: England
- C: The Netherlands
- D: Germany

6

Hernan Crespo was a member of which country's 2006 squad?

- A: England
- B: Italy
- C: Spain
- D: Argentina

7

Which Brazilian midfielder featured in the 1982 and 1986 World Cups?

- A: Aristotle
- B: Plato
- C: Socrates
- D: Pythagoras

8

Which country knocked England out of the World Cup in both 1986 and 1998?

- A: Spain
- B: Brazil
- C: Argentina
- D: Germany

If you would like to use your 50:50 please turn to page 297
If you would like to use your Ask The Audience please turn to page 318
Turn to the answer section on page 332 to find out if you've won £1000!

5 ◆ £1000 WORLD CUP

9

To which World Cup finals did England travel as reigning world champions?

- A: 1958
- B: 1962
- C: 1966
- D: 1970

10

What media term is given to a group in which any team could qualify or be eliminated?

- A: Group of Doom
- B: Group of Hell
- C: Group of Death
- D: Group of Fate

11

Which country came third at the 2006 World Cup finals?

- A: Croatia
- B: France
- C: Germany
- D: Portugal

12

Which of these made their only appearance to date in the World Cup finals in 1958?

- A: Scotland
- B: Northern Ireland
- C: Wales
- D: Republic of Ireland

If you would like to use your 50:50 please turn to page 297
If you would like to use your Ask The Audience please turn to page 318–319
Turn to the answer section on page 332 to find out if you've won £1000!

5 ◆ £1000 WORLD CUP

13

At the 2006 World Cup, which team reached the semi-finals for the first time since 1966?

- A: France
- B: Germany
- C: Italy
- D: Portugal

14

In the 1986 World Cup finals, who played against Brazil on his 41st birthday?

- A: Pat Jennings
- B: Mal Donaghy
- C: David McCreery
- D: Jim Quinn

15

Which is the most populous nation yet to send its national team to the World Cup finals?

- A: China
- B: Russia
- C: USA
- D: India

16

By four years, who was the oldest member of England's 2006 World Cup finals squad?

- A: Scott Carson
- B: Ashley Cole
- C: Jermaine Jenas
- D: David James

If you would like to use your 50:50 please turn to page 297
If you would like to use your Ask The Audience please turn to page 319
Turn to the answer section on page 332 to find out if you've won £1000!

5 ◆ £1000 WORLD CUP

17

What was Footix, the official mascot of the 1998 World Cup finals in France?

- A: Lion
- B: Garlic bulb
- C: Cockerel
- D: Onion

18

Which of FIFA's confederations provided the most competing teams for the 2010 World Cup finals?

- A: OFC
- B: UEFA
- C: CONMEBOL
- D: CONCACAF

19

Which of these was not part of the Oceania 2010 World Cup qualifying zone?

- A: New Zealand
- B: New Caledonia
- C: Fiji
- D: Bahrain

20

In 2009, whose handball led to a French winning goal in a World Cup play-off game?

- A: William Gallas
- B: Thierry Henry
- C: Nicolas Anelka
- D: Alou Diarra

If you would like to use your 50:50 please turn to page 297
If you would like to use your Ask The Audience please turn to page 319
Turn to the answer section on page 332 to find out if you've won £1000!

5 ◆ £1000 WORLD CUP

21

Zakumi, the mascot of the 2010 World Cup finals, has what colour hair?

- A: Red
- B: Blue
- C: Black
- D: Green

22

Which country qualified for the 2010 World Cup, twenty-eight years after last doing so?

- A: New Zealand
- B: Chile
- C: USA
- D: Portugal

23

Which European country asked to be included as the thirty-third team at the 2010 World Cup finals?

- A: Republic of Ireland
- B: Czech Republic
- C: Russia
- D: Ukraine

24

Who has not won the Golden Shoe at the World Cup finals?

- A: David Beckham
- B: Ronaldo
- C: Paolo Rossi
- D: Mario Kempes

If you would like to use your 50:50 please turn to page 297
If you would like to use your Ask The Audience please turn to page 319
Turn to the answer section on page 332 to find out if you've won £1000!

5 ◆ £1000 WORLD CUP

25

Who was England's top scorer at the 2002 World Cup with two goals?

- A: Michael Owen
- B: David Beckham
- C: Sol Campbell
- D: Emile Heskey

26

Joe Jordan is which country's leading World Cup scorer?

- A: Scotland
- B: Wales
- C: Northern Ireland
- D: England

27

What was the name of the official ball used at the 2002 tournament?

- A: Fevernova
- B: Bossanova
- C: Supernova
- D: Casanova

28

In which year did Michael Owen make his World Cup finals debut?

- A: 1986
- B: 1990
- C: 1998
- D: 2002

If you would like to use your 50:50 please turn to page 297
If you would like to use your Ask The Audience please turn to page 319
Turn to the answer section on page 332 to find out if you've won £1000!

5 ◆ £1000 WORLD CUP

29

On the World Cup website, which team from Asia is abbreviated as MYA?

- A: Malaysia
- B: Maldives
- C: Mongolia
- D: Myanmar

30

The Adidas Golden Ball is awarded for what?

- A: Top goalscorer
- B: Best player
- C: Best sport
- D: Best defender

31

Which team was captained by Fabio Cannavaro at the 2006 World Cup finals?

- A: Germany
- B: Spain
- C: Switzerland
- D: Italy

32

Zakumi, the mascot of the 2010 World Cup finals, wears what colour shorts?

- A: Green
- B: White
- C: Gold
- D: Red

If you would like to use your 50:50 please turn to page 297
If you would like to use your Ask The Audience please turn to page 319
Turn to the answer section on page 332 to find out if you've won £1000!

5 ◆ £1000 WORLD CUP

33

Who were dubbed the 'Kings of football' by the Brazilian media at their first World Cup in 1950?

- A: England
- B: Spain
- C: Sweden
- D: Yugoslavia

34

Venue for a 2010 qualifying play-off, the Westpac Stadium is known by what other name?

- A: The Biscuit Barrel
- B: The Cake Tin
- C: The Cookie Jar
- D: The Muffin Tray

35

At the 1998 World Cup, which team ranked 74 in the world, became the lowest-ranked qualifier?

- A: Colombia
- B: Romania
- C: Nigeria
- D: Scotland

36

Which CONCACAF member nation has qualified for the most World Cup finals?

- A: Guatemala
- B: Honduras
- C: Mexico
- D: El Salvador

If you would like to use your 50:50 please turn to page 297
If you would like to use your Ask The Audience please turn to page 319
Turn to the answer section on page 332 to find out if you've won £1000!

5 ◆ £1000 WORLD CUP

37

In what position does the Italian World Cup winner Gianluigi Buffon play?

- A: Centre forward
- B: Striker
- C: Goalkeeper
- D: Defender

38

Who was England's top scorer in the qualifying matches for the 2010 World Cup finals?

- A: Joe Cole
- B: Wayne Rooney
- C: John Terry
- D: Steven Gerrard

39

Who scored England's only goal in the 2002 World Cup defeat by Brazil?

- A: Michael Owen
- B: David Beckham
- C: Emile Heskey
- D: Darius Vassell

40

Until 2003, Serbia appeared on the international stage under the banner of which country?

- A: Hungary
- B: Poland
- C: Yugoslavia
- D: Italy

If you would like to use your 50:50 please turn to page 297
If you would like to use your Ask The Audience please turn to page 319
Turn to the answer section on page 332 to find out if you've won £1000!

5 ◆ £1000 WORLD CUP

41

What nationality is the manager, and Lev Yashin Award winner, Michel Preud'homme?

- A: Swiss
- B: Belgian
- C: French
- D: Canadian

42

What was Naranjito, the official mascot of the 1982 World Cup finals hosted by Spain?

- A: Footballer
- B: Orange
- C: Hot pepper
- D: Lion

43

Which was the highest-ranked team in Group A at the 2010 World Cup finals?

- A: South Africa
- B: Mexico
- C: France
- D: Uruguay

44

At the 1950 World Cup, which team consisted of teachers, a dishwasher and a hearse driver?

- A: England
- B: Italy
- C: USA
- D: Brazil

If you would like to use your 50:50 please turn to page 297
If you would like to use your Ask The Audience please turn to page 319
Turn to the answer section on page 332 to find out if you've won £1000!

5 ◆ £1000 WORLD CUP

45

Against whom were South Africa drawn to play in the opening game of the 2010 World Cup finals?

- A: Uruguay
- B: Mexico
- C: France
- D: Japan

46

Who did not qualify for 2010 from the European zone by virtue of topping their group?

- A: Germany
- B: Spain
- C: England
- D: Ukraine

If you would like to use your 50:50 please turn to page 297
If you would like to use your Ask The Audience please turn to page 319
Turn to the answer section on page 332 to find out if you've won £1000!

5 ◆ £1000 EUROPEAN

1

Prior to 2009/10, which of these Italian teams has not won what is now the Champions League?

- A: Lazio
- B: Juventus
- C: Inter Milan
- D: AC Milan

2

Besides Benfica, what other Portuguese team has won the European Cup or Champions League title?

- A: Nacional
- B: Rio Ave
- C: Porto
- D: Braga

3

In the Europa League, what is the next stage after the group matches?

- A: Round of 4
- B: Round of 8
- C: Round of 16
- D: Round of 32

4

By what name was the Champions League formerly known?

- A: UEFA Cup
- B: Cup Winners' Cup
- C: European Cup
- D: Fairs Cup

If you would like to use your 50:50 please turn to page 297
If you would like to use your Ask The Audience please turn to page 319
Turn to the answer section on page 332 to find out if you've won £1000!

5 ◆ £1000 EUROPEAN

5

In 2008, who did Chelsea play in the first all-English Champions League final?

- A: Manchester City
- B: Arsenal
- C: Manchester United
- D: Liverpool

6

The only man with two European Championship winners' medals, Rainer Bonhof played for whom?

- A: West Germany
- B: Turkey
- C: Greece
- D: Sweden

7

Red and which other colour form the stripes on Barcelona's first-choice shirts?

- A: White
- B: Black
- C: Yellow
- D: Blue

8

In which city would a local derby take place between Besiktas and Fenerbahçe?

- A: Sofia
- B: Moscow
- C: Prague
- D: Istanbul

If you would like to use your 50:50 please turn to page 297
If you would like to use your Ask The Audience please turn to page 319
Turn to the answer section on page 332 to find out if you've won £1000!

5 ◆ £1000 EUROPEAN

9

In the early twentieth century, the shirts worn by Notts County inspired which team to imitate them?

- A: Juventus
- B: Borussia Dortmund
- C: Paris Saint-Germain
- D: Benfica

10

From which Spanish club did Newcastle United sign Michael Owen in 2005?

- A: Real Madrid
- B: Barcelona
- C: Real Betis
- D: Celta Vigo

11

Complete the name of the Italian striker, Alessandro . . .

- A: Della Francesca
- B: Del Piero
- C: Del Monte
- D: Del Amore

12

Shelbourne, Bohemians and Finn Harps are clubs in which country?

- A: The Netherlands
- B: Greece
- C: Wales
- D: Republic of Ireland

If you would like to use your 50:50 please turn to page 297
If you would like to use your Ask The Audience please turn to page 319
Turn to the answer section on page 332 to find out if you've won £1000!

5 ◆ £1000 EUROPEAN

13

Which European politician is the owner of AC Milan?

- A: Angela Merkel
- B: Vladimir Putin
- C: Nicolas Sarkozy
- D: Silvio Berlusconi

14

In which year did the European Cup become the Champions League?

- A: 2002
- B: 1992
- C: 1982
- D: 1972

15

Steaua Bucharest were the first European Cup winners from which country?

- A: Romania
- B: France
- C: Portugal
- D: Denmark

16

In 2001, which English club won the UEFA Cup by virtue of the golden goal ruling?

- A: Liverpool
- B: Sheffield United
- C: Sunderland
- D: Leeds United

If you would like to use your 50:50 please turn to page 297
If you would like to use your Ask The Audience please turn to page 319
Turn to the answer section on page 332 to find out if you've won £1000!

5 ◆ £1000 EUROPEAN

17

Shakhtar Donetsk, the 2009 UEFA Cup winners, are from which country?

- A: Denmark
- B: Switzerland
- C: Ukraine
- D: Belgium

18

Which of these is not, or was not, considered to be a UEFA competition?

- A: Cup Winners' Cup
- B: UEFA Cup
- C: Champions League
- D: Fairs Cup

19

Which team won the 1992 European Championship, defeating Germany 2-0 in the final?

- A: Belgium
- B: Finland
- C: Denmark
- D: Iceland

20

Since 1998, the Stade Louis II in Monaco has always hosted which final?

- A: UEFA Cup
- B: Champions League
- C: UEFA Super Cup
- D: Cup Winners' Cup

If you would like to use your 50:50 please turn to pages 297–298
If you would like to use your Ask The Audience please turn to page 319
Turn to the answer section on page 332 to find out if you've won £1000!

5 ◆ £1000 EUROPEAN

21

How many handles does the Champions League trophy have?

- A: None
- B: Two
- C: Three
- D: Four

22

Who is the only Scottish manager to have won the European Cup or Champions League twice?

- A: Matt Busby
- B: Jock Stein
- C: Alex Ferguson
- D: Walter Smith

If you would like to use your 50:50 please turn to page 298
If you would like to use your Ask The Audience please turn to page 319
Turn to the answer section on page 332 to find out if you've won £1000!

5 ◆ £1000 DOMESTIC

1

The two main clubs from which city met in a Carling Cup semi-final in 2010?

- A: Manchester
- B: Bristol
- C: Sheffield
- D: Nottingham

2

A statue of which famous player is situated outside the Park End at Goodison Park?

- A: Jimmy Greaves
- B: Alan Shearer
- C: Dixie Dean
- D: George Best

3

In 2009/10, the Principality Building Society sponsored which country's top division?

- A: Scotland
- B: England
- C: Wales
- D: Northern Ireland

4

Which club arguably came into existence because of Everton's row over rent?

- A: Manchester City
- B: Crystal Palace
- C: Leeds United
- D: Liverpool

If you would like to use your 50:50 please turn to page 298
If you would like to use your Ask The Audience please turn to page 319
Turn to the answer section on page 332 to find out if you've won £1000!

5 ◆ £1000 DOMESTIC

5

A red and white scarf appears on the badge of which club?

- A: Manchester City
- B: Leeds United
- C: Southampton
- D: Blackburn Rovers

6

By what nickname was Stuart Pearce affectionately known during his playing days?

- A: Doc
- B: Sicknote
- C: Psycho
- D: Cuddles

7

Blackburn Rovers wear halved shirts of which two colours?

- A: Green and yellow
- B: Blue and white
- C: Red and gold
- D: Pink and orange

8

As of January 2010, who has made over 800 appearances for Manchester United?

- A: Ryan Giggs
- B: Gary Neville
- C: Paul Scholes
- D: Rio Ferdinand

If you would like to use your 50:50 please turn to page 298
If you would like to use your Ask The Audience please turn to page 319
Turn to the answer section on page 332 to find out if you've won £1000!

5 ◆ £1000 DOMESTIC

9

Which of these is not a nickname applied to West Bromwich Albion?

- A: Hornets
- B: Throstles
- C: Baggies
- D: Albion

10

Which club has not been in the Premier League continually since its inception?

- A: Manchester United
- B: Manchester City
- C: Arsenal
- D: Chelsea

11

In which year did the FA Cup final return to Wembley?

- A: 2005
- B: 2006
- C: 2007
- D: 2008

12

Which of these Manchester City players is Irish?

- A: Stuart Taylor
- B: Shay Given
- C: Martin Petrov
- D: Gareth Barry

If you would like to use your 50:50 please turn to page 298
If you would like to use your Ask The Audience please turn to page 319
Turn to the answer section on page 332 to find out if you've won £1000!

5 ◆ £1000 DOMESTIC

13

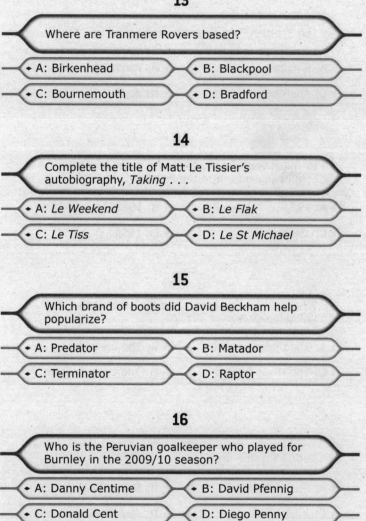

Where are Tranmere Rovers based?

- A: Birkenhead
- B: Blackpool
- C: Bournemouth
- D: Bradford

14

Complete the title of Matt Le Tissier's autobiography, *Taking . . .*

- A: *Le Weekend*
- B: *Le Flak*
- C: *Le Tiss*
- D: *Le St Michael*

15

Which brand of boots did David Beckham help popularize?

- A: Predator
- B: Matador
- C: Terminator
- D: Raptor

16

Who is the Peruvian goalkeeper who played for Burnley in the 2009/10 season?

- A: Danny Centime
- B: David Pfennig
- C: Donald Cent
- D: Diego Penny

If you would like to use your 50:50 please turn to page 298
If you would like to use your Ask The Audience please turn to page 320
Turn to the answer section on pages 332–333 to find out if you've won £1000!

5 ◆ £1000 DOMESTIC

17

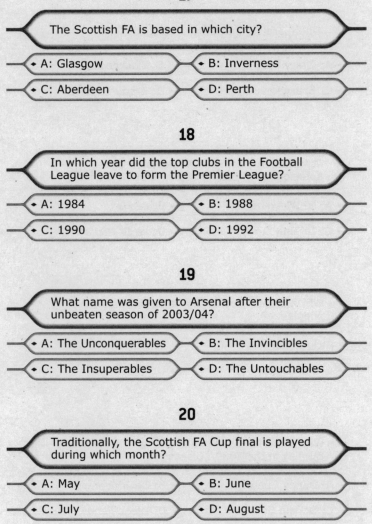

The Scottish FA is based in which city?

- A: Glasgow
- B: Inverness
- C: Aberdeen
- D: Perth

18

In which year did the top clubs in the Football League leave to form the Premier League?

- A: 1984
- B: 1988
- C: 1990
- D: 1992

19

What name was given to Arsenal after their unbeaten season of 2003/04?

- A: The Unconquerables
- B: The Invincibles
- C: The Insuperables
- D: The Untouchables

20

Traditionally, the Scottish FA Cup final is played during which month?

- A: May
- B: June
- C: July
- D: August

If you would like to use your 50:50 please turn to page 298
If you would like to use your Ask The Audience please turn to page 320
Turn to the answer section on page 333 to find out if you've won £1000!

5 ◆ £1000 DOMESTIC

21

By what nickname was the Liverpool and England defender Emlyn Hughes sometimes known?

- A: Crazy Feet
- B: Crazy Horse
- C: Crazy Kid
- D: Crazy Scouse

22

Which energy company announced its sponsorship of the FA Cup in 2006?

- A: ZEST 4
- B: e.on
- C: Virgin Energy
- D: Manweb

If you would like to use your 50:50 please turn to page 298
If you would like to use your Ask The Audience please turn to page 320
Turn to the answer section on page 333 to find out if you've won £1000!

50:50

15	£1 MILLION
14	£5000,00
13	£250,000
12	£125,000
11	£64,000
10	£32,000
9	£16,000
8	£8,000
7	£4,000
6	£2,000
5	£1,000
4	£500
3	£300
2	£200
1	£100

6 ◆ £2000 WORLD CUP

1

Which team went into the 2006 World Cup finals against the backdrop of a match-fixing scandal?

- A: Brazil
- B: England
- C: Italy
- D: Portugal

2

Prior to 2010, which of these countries has Italy not defeated in a World Cup final?

- A: Czechoslovakia
- B: Germany
- C: Brazil
- D: France

3

How many times have Italy been runners-up to Brazil in a World Cup final?

- A: Three
- B: Twice
- C: Once
- D: Never

4

Which country qualified for the 2010 World Cup finals in 2004?

- A: England
- B: Italy
- C: Brazil
- D: South Africa

If you would like to use your 50:50 please turn to page 299
If you would like to use your Ask The Audience please turn to page 320
Turn to the answer section on page 333 to find out if you've won £2000!

6 ◆ £2000 WORLD CUP

5

For which 2010 World Cup qualifying nation does Didier Drogba play?

- A: Malawi
- B: Côte d'Ivoire
- C: Ghana
- D: Cameroon

6

For which team did Miroslav Klose score five goals in the 2006 World Cup finals?

- A: Croatia
- B: Germany
- C: Czech Republic
- D: Poland

7

Which of these was a match played during the World Cup finals?

- A: North v South Vietnam
- B: East v West Germany
- C: China v Taiwan
- D: East v West Pakistan

8

Which of these African teams has played in the World Cup finals?

- A: Senegal
- B: Sierra Leone
- C: Sudan
- D: Somalia

If you would like to use your 50:50 please turn to page 299
If you would like to use your Ask The Audience please turn to page 320
Turn to the answer section on page 333 to find out if you've won £2000!

6 ◆ £2000 WORLD CUP

9

For what is the Lev Yashin Award presented at World Cup tournaments?

- A: Most valued player
- B: Best attacking play
- C: Fair play
- D: Best goalkeeper

10

Who was head coach of the Republic of Ireland in their 2010 World Cup campaign?

- A: Nigel Worthington
- B: Marcello Lippi
- C: Pim Verbeek
- D: Giovanni Trapattoni

11

Which of these 2010 stadia is in Johannesburg?

- A: Green Point
- B: Peter Mokaba
- C: Ellis Park
- D: Nelson Mandela

12

Bert Van Marwijk was head coach of which team during their 2010 World Cup campaign?

- A: Ghana
- B: The Netherlands
- C: Côte d'Ivoire
- D: Switzerland

If you would like to use your 50:50 please turn to page 299
If you would like to use your Ask The Audience please turn to page 320
Turn to the answer section on page 333 to find out if you've won £2000!

6 ◆ £2000 WORLD CUP

13

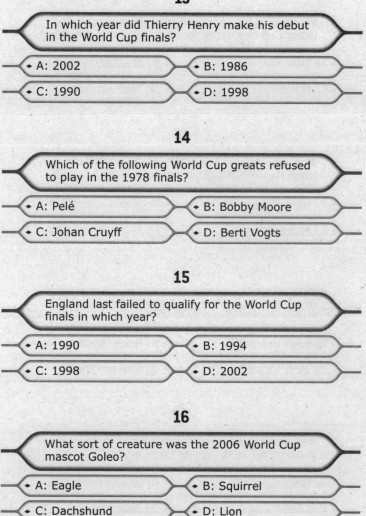

In which year did Thierry Henry make his debut in the World Cup finals?

- A: 2002
- B: 1986
- C: 1990
- D: 1998

14

Which of the following World Cup greats refused to play in the 1978 finals?

- A: Pelé
- B: Bobby Moore
- C: Johan Cruyff
- D: Berti Vogts

15

England last failed to qualify for the World Cup finals in which year?

- A: 1990
- B: 1994
- C: 1998
- D: 2002

16

What sort of creature was the 2006 World Cup mascot Goleo?

- A: Eagle
- B: Squirrel
- C: Dachshund
- D: Lion

If you would like to use your 50:50 please turn to page 299
If you would like to use your Ask The Audience please turn to page 320
Turn to the answer section on page 333 to find out if you've won £2000!

6 ◆ £2000 WORLD CUP

17

In 2006, which country making its debut in the World Cup finals was drawn in England's group?

- A: Ukraine
- B: Angola
- C: Trinidad & Tobago
- D: Togo

18

Who pioneered the style of 'total football' to reach two World Cup finals in the 1970s?

- A: West Germany
- B: Brazil
- C: Argentina
- D: The Netherlands

19

Which former England manager narrowly failed to help Australia qualify in 1998?

- A: Ron Greenwood
- B: Bobby Robson
- C: Terry Venables
- D: Graham Taylor

20

Which team won the 1962 World Cup but were knocked out at the group stage in 1966?

- A: West Germany
- B: Uruguay
- C: Brazil
- D: Italy

If you would like to use your 50:50 please turn to page 299
If you would like to use your Ask The Audience please turn to page 320
Turn to the answer section on page 333 to find out if you've won £2000!

6 ◆ £2000 WORLD CUP

21

In which year was the Jules Rimet trophy presented for the last time?

- A: 1966
- B: 1970
- C: 1974
- D: 1978

22

Which former World Cup winners qualified for South Africa before the others?

- A: Italy
- B: Germany
- C: Brazil
- D: Argentina

23

Which two former champions were drawn together in Group A for the 2010 World Cup finals?

- A: England and Italy
- B: Uruguay and France
- C: Brazil and Germany
- D: Argentina and Italy

24

Coca-Cola Park in Johannesburg is better known by what previous name?

- A: Edwards Park
- B: Everard Park
- C: Ellis Park
- D: Edmonds Park

If you would like to use your 50:50 please turn to page 299
If you would like to use your Ask The Audience please turn to page 320
Turn to the answer section on page 333 to find out if you've won £2000!

6 ◆ £2000 WORLD CUP

25

Which 17-year-old played against Yugoslavia in the pool stages of the 1982 World Cup finals?

- A: Diego Maradona
- B: Hristo Stoichkov
- C: Jürgen Klinsmann
- D: Norman Whiteside

26

Which country took part in the World Cup preliminary competition for the first time for the 2010 tournament?

- A: Moldova
- B: Montenegro
- C: Malta
- D: Macedonia FYR

27

Who scored a penalty to give England a win against Argentina in the 2002 World Cup?

- A: Paul Scholes
- B: Michael Owen
- C: Emile Heskey
- D: David Beckham

28

In which year was the first World Cup after World War II?

- A: 1946
- B: 1948
- C: 1950
- D: 1952

If you would like to use your 50:50 please turn to page 299
If you would like to use your Ask The Audience please turn to page 320
Turn to the answer section on page 333 to find out if you've won £2000!

6 ◆ £2000 WORLD CUP

29

In which year was the last World Cup held before the outbreak of World War II?

- A: 1938
- B: 1936
- C: 1934
- D: 1932

30

Who failed to qualify for four consecutive World Cups but reached the final of the next one?

- A: England
- B: The Netherlands
- C: Spain
- D: Portugal

31

Which was the lowest-ranked team drawn in Group G for the 2010 World Cup finals?

- A: Côte d'Ivoire
- B: Portugal
- C: North Korea
- D: Brazil

32

Which of these is a star player in the Cameroon 2010 World Cup squad?

- A: Samuel Iti'i
- B: Samuel Oto'o
- C: Samuel Eto'o
- D: Samuel Ata'a

If you would like to use your 50:50 please turn to page 299
If you would like to use your Ask The Audience please turn to page 320
Turn to the answer section on page 333 to find out if you've won £2000!

6 ◆ £2000 WORLD CUP

33

Theofanis Gekas was which country's top scorer in their 2010 World Cup qualifying campaign?

- A: England
- B: USA
- C: Greece
- D: Nigeria

34

Which was the lowest-ranked team drawn in Group D for the 2010 World Cup finals?

- A: Australia
- B: Ghana
- C: Serbia
- D: Germany

35

Radomir Antic was manager of which team during their 2010 campaign?

- A: Japan
- B: USA
- C: Serbia
- D: The Netherlands

36

Who managed the Australian team during their 2010 campaign?

- A: Joachim Löw
- B: Raddy Antic
- C: Morten Olsen
- D: Pim Verbeek

If you would like to use your 50:50 please turn to page 299
If you would like to use your Ask The Audience please turn to page 320
Turn to the answer section on page 333 to find out if you've won £2000!

6 ◆ £2000 WORLD CUP

37

What was the name of the dog who found the stolen World Cup trophy in 1966?

- A: Scamp
- B: Buster
- C: Pickles
- D: Nipper

38

In which position did Oliver Kahn play for Germany at the 2002 World Cup?

- A: Goalkeeper
- B: Sweeper
- C: Midfield
- D: Striker

39

Bats, Tigana and Giresse all played for which team in the 1986 World Cup?

- A: Italy
- B: France
- C: Brazil
- D: Hungary

40

Whose goal against England in 1986 is known as the World Cup goal of the twentieth century?

- A: Gheorghe Hagi
- B: Roberto Baggio
- C: Diego Maradona
- D: Vincenzo Scifo

If you would like to use your 50:50 please turn to page 299
If you would like to use your Ask The Audience please turn to page 320
Turn to the answer section on page 333 to find out if you've won £2000!

6 ◆ £2000 WORLD CUP

41

Who was England coach at the 1954 World Cup finals?

- A: Alf Ramsey
- B: Walter Winterbottom
- C: Matt Busby
- D: Bill Shankly

42

Against whom did France face a play-off to decide qualification for the 2010 World Cup?

- A: Republic of Ireland
- B: Bulgaria
- C: Cyprus
- D: Montenegro

43

In 1990, who became only the second man to win the World Cup as both player and manager?

- A: Carlos Bilardo
- B: Sebastio Lazaroni
- C: Luis Suarez
- D: Franz Beckenbauer

44

Who is the only manager to guide England in four World Cup final tournaments?

- A: Bobby Robson
- B: Ron Greenwood
- C: Alf Ramsey
- D: Walter Winterbottom

If you would like to use your 50:50 please turn to page 299
If you would like to use your Ask The Audience please turn to page 320
Turn to the answer section on page 333 to find out if you've won £2000!

6 ◆ £2000 EUROPEAN

1

Which national team is sometimes nicknamed 'The Clockwork Orange'?

- A: South Africa
- B: The Netherlands
- C: Germany
- D: India

2

By what nickname is the Italian club Juventus commonly known?

- A: Old Man
- B: Old Lady
- C: Old Friend
- D: Old Enemy

3

Which national team are nicknamed 'Red Devils'?

- A: Belgium
- B: Greece
- C: Portugal
- D: The Netherlands

4

Which credit-card company is a main sponsor of the Champions League?

- A: Visa
- B: MasterCard
- C: American Express
- D: Citibank

If you would like to use your 50:50 please turn to page 299
If you would like to use your Ask The Audience please turn to page 320
Turn to the answer section on page 333 to find out if you've won £2000!

6 ◆ £2000 EUROPEAN

5

Which former England manager took over a Dutch league team in June 2009?

- A: Terry Venables
- B: Kevin Keegan
- C: Peter Taylor
- D: Steve McClaren

6

Which former Brazilian international was appointed head coach at AC Milan in 2009?

- A: Michelangelo
- B: Donatello
- C: Raphael
- D: Leonardo

7

What nickname was given to Franz Beckenbauer?

- A: The Colonel
- B: The General
- C: The Kaiser
- D: The Führer

8

Complete the footballer's name, Jan Vennegoor of . . .

- A: Haarlemmermeer
- B: s'Hertogenbosch
- C: Hellendoom
- D: Hesselink

If you would like to use your 50:50 please turn to page 299
If you would like to use your Ask The Audience please turn to page 320
Turn to the answer section on page 333 to find out if you've won £2000!

6 ◆ £2000 EUROPEAN

9

At which Spanish club did Gary Lineker spend three years in the 1980s?

- A: Barcelona
- B: Real Madrid
- C: Atlético Madrid
- D: Valencia

10

For which country did Michel Platini play international football?

- A: The Netherlands
- B: France
- C: Belgium
- D: Italy

11

For its first five years, the European Cup was won by a team from which country?

- A: West Germany
- B: Italy
- C: Spain
- D: Soviet Union

12

FC Basel was the only club from which country in the group stages of the 2009/10 Europa League?

- A: Portugal
- B: Switzerland
- C: Slovakia
- D: Denmark

If you would like to use your 50:50 please turn to page 299
If you would like to use your Ask The Audience please turn to page 320
Turn to the answer section on page 333 to find out if you've won £2000!

6 ◆ £2000 EUROPEAN

13

How many handles does the Europa League trophy have?

- A: None
- B: Two
- C: Three
- D: Four

14

What has not happened at the final stages of the European Championship since 1980?

- A: Third/fourth place play-off
- B: Singing of anthems
- C: Use of floodlights
- D: A no-score draw

15

From 1976/77 to 1981/82, the European Cup was won six times by teams from which country?

- A: England
- B: The Netherlands
- C: France
- D: Spain

16

Unirea Urziceni is a club from which country?

- A: Portugal
- B: Romania
- C: Denmark
- D: Cyprus

If you would like to use your 50:50 please turn to page 299
If you would like to use your Ask The Audience please turn to page 320–321
Turn to the answer section on page 333 to find out if you've won £2000!

6 ◆ £2000 EUROPEAN

17

Which country had the maximum of four teams in the group stages of the 2009/10 Champions League?

- A: Russia
- B: Belgium
- C: England
- D: The Netherlands

18

Besides Germany, which other country has a Bundesliga?

- A: Finland
- B: Bulgaria
- C: Czech Republic
- D: Austria

19

The Ernst Happel Stadium in Vienna hosted which final in 2008?

- A: Euro 2008
- B: Champions League
- C: UEFA Cup
- D: UEFA Super Cup

20

Which was the first 'non-Latin' team to win the European Cup?

- A: Celtic
- B: Ajax
- C: Manchester United
- D: Bayern Munich

If you would like to use your 50:50 please turn to page 299
If you would like to use your Ask The Audience please turn to page 321
Turn to the answer section on page 333 to find out if you've won £2000!

6 ◆ £2000 EUROPEAN

21

Which country won Euro 2008?

- A: Germany
- B: Russia
- C: Spain
- D: Turkey

22

In Spain, El Clásico is the match between Real Madrid and which other team?

- A: Barcelona
- B: Atlético Madrid
- C: Real Zaragoza
- D: Valencia

If you would like to use your 50:50 please turn to page 300
If you would like to use your Ask The Audience please turn to page 321
Turn to the answer section on page 333 to find out if you've won £2000!

6 ◆ £2000 DOMESTIC

1

What nationality is the defender Alex, who played for Chelsea in 2009/10?

- A: Brazilian
- B: Belgian
- C: Bolivian
- D: Bhutanese

2

Which of these is not a regular brand of football boots?

- A: Adidas
- B: Umbro
- C: Reebok
- D: Speedo

3

Which England footballer won his 100th cap in a friendly against France in March 2008?

- A: David Beckham
- B: David James
- C: Steven Gerrard
- D: Rio Ferdinand

4

For which of these clubs did Alan Shearer never play?

- A: Southampton
- B: Blackburn Rovers
- C: Liverpool
- D: Newcastle United

If you would like to use your 50:50 please turn to page 300
If you would like to use your Ask The Audience please turn to page 321
Turn to the answer section on page 333 to find out if you've won £2000!

6 ◆ £2000 DOMESTIC

5

Which of these stadia stands by the river Taff?

- A: Craven Cottage
- B: Meadow Lane
- C: Riverside Stadium
- D: Millennium Stadium

6

Which 'first' occurred in the 2005 FA Cup final?

- A: Golden goal
- B: Pitch invasion
- C: Female streak
- D: Penalty shoot-out

7

Who beat Everton in the 2009 FA Cup final?

- A: Chelsea
- B: Manchester United
- C: Arsenal
- D: Birmingham City

8

Of which club was Alan Sugar the chairman from 1991 to 2001?

- A: Arsenal
- B: Tottenham Hotspur
- C: Fulham
- D: West Ham United

If you would like to use your 50:50 please turn to page 300
If you would like to use your Ask The Audience please turn to page 321
Turn to the answer section on page 333 to find out if you've won £2000!

6 ◆ £2000 DOMESTIC

9

Wigan Athletic's DW Stadium was previously known by what initials?

- A: MFI
- B: JJB
- C: B & Q
- D: HSBC

10

In 2009, the FA agreed a new deal for which brewery to continue to sponsor England?

- A: Carling
- B: Fosters
- C: Carlsberg
- D: Heineken

11

Which of these clubs has played in the Premier League prior to the 2010/11 season?

- A: Swansea City
- B: Stockport County
- C: Southend United
- D: Swindon Town

12

In May 2009, which club won the Scottish Premier League title?

- A: Celtic
- B: Rangers
- C: Hearts
- D: Aberdeen

If you would like to use your 50:50 please turn to page 300
If you would like to use your Ask The Audience please turn to page 321
Turn to the answer section on page 333 to find out if you've won £2000!

6 ◆ £2000 DOMESTIC

13

David Moyes was appointed manager of which club in March 2002?

- A: Everton
- B: Leeds United
- C: Celtic
- D: Burnley

14

Who did John Toshack succeed as Welsh national manager in 2004?

- A: Mike England
- B: Mark Hughes
- C: Mike Smith
- D: Bobby Gould

15

Chris Baird, Steven Davis and Colin Coates have all been capped by which country?

- A: Wales
- B: Scotland
- C: Northern Ireland
- D: Republic of Ireland

16

Which England manager went on to coach the Australian national team?

- A: Don Revie
- B: Alf Ramsey
- C: Bobby Robson
- D: Terry Venables

If you would like to use your 50:50 please turn to page 300
If you would like to use your Ask The Audience please turn to page 321
Turn to the answer section on page 333 to find out if you've won £2000!

6 ◆ £2000 DOMESTIC

17

Who, after the last match at the old Wembley stadium, resigned as England's manager?

- A: Bobby Robson
- B: Terry Venables
- C: Kevin Keegan
- D: Glenn Hoddle

18

In 2006, which club sold 16-year-old Theo Walcott to Arsenal for a potential £12.5 million?

- A: Crystal Palace
- B: Reading
- C: Southampton
- D: Portsmouth

19

The line 'And the sweet silver song of the lark' features in which club's anthem?

- A: Newcastle United
- B: West Ham United
- C: Liverpool
- D: Chelsea

20

At which club's ground is there a stand named after Jackie Milburn?

- A: Everton
- B: Liverpool
- C: Newcastle United
- D: Leeds United

If you would like to use your 50:50 please turn to page 300
If you would like to use your Ask The Audience please turn to page 321
Turn to the answer section on page 333 to find out if you've won £2000!

6 ◆ £2000 DOMESTIC

21

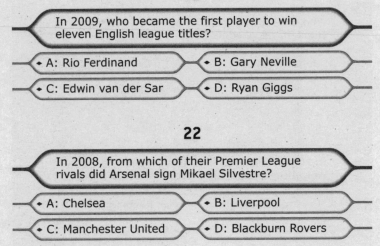

In 2009, who became the first player to win eleven English league titles?

- A: Rio Ferdinand
- B: Gary Neville
- C: Edwin van der Sar
- D: Ryan Giggs

22

In 2008, from which of their Premier League rivals did Arsenal sign Mikael Silvestre?

- A: Chelsea
- B: Liverpool
- C: Manchester United
- D: Blackburn Rovers

If you would like to use your 50:50 please turn to page 300
If you would like to use your Ask The Audience please turn to page 321
Turn to the answer section on page 333 to find out if you've won £2000!

50:50

15	£1 MILLION
14	£5000,00
13	£250,000
12	£125,000
11	£64,000
10	£32,000
9	£16,000
8	£8,000
7	£4,000
6	£2,000
5	£1,000
4	£500
3	£300
2	£200
1	£100

7 ◆ £4000 WORLD CUP

1

Prior to 2010, which of the seven World Cup-winning countries did not do so as the host nation?

- A: Italy
- B: Brazil
- C: Germany
- D: Uruguay

2

In which decade did Italy win consecutive World Cups?

- A: 1930s
- B: 1950s
- C: 1980s
- D: 1990s

3

Which of these 2006 England World Cup squad members was then signed to a foreign club?

- A: Gary Neville
- B: Ashley Cole
- C: John Terry
- D: David Beckham

4

In 2006, which African nation made its first appearance at the World Cup finals?

- A: Angola
- B: Benin
- C: Chad
- D: Djibouti

If you would like to use your 50:50 please turn to page 301
If you would like to use your Ask The Audience please turn to page 321
Turn to the answer section on page 333 to find out if you've won £4000!

7 ◆ £4000 WORLD CUP

5

To date, which country's only appearance in the World Cup finals was in 1970?

- A: Iraq
- B: Iran
- C: Israel
- D: India

6

Which reigning champions went to the next World Cup finals and did not score a single goal?

- A: Uruguay
- B: England
- C: France
- D: Argentina

7

Which team memorably defeated Argentina in the opening match of the 1990 World Cup finals?

- A: Costa Rica
- B: Republic of Ireland
- C: Cameroon
- D: UAE

8

Which England player did not miss a penalty in the shoot-out against Portugal in 2006?

- A: Hargreaves
- B: Lampard
- C: Gerrard
- D: Carragher

If you would like to use your 50:50 please turn to page 301
If you would like to use your Ask The Audience please turn to page 321
Turn to the answer section on page 333 to find out if you've won £4000!

7 ◆ £4000 WORLD CUP

9

Which of England's opponents in the 1990 World Cup were nicknamed the 'Indomitable Lions'?

- A: Egypt
- B: The Netherlands
- C: Cameroon
- D: Belgium

10

Who was the sole survivor from France's 1998 World Cup-winning team in their 2010 campaign?

- A: Nicolas Anelka
- B: Sidney Govou
- C: William Gallas
- D: Thierry Henry

11

Who were reigning champions Italy drawn against in their opening game in South Africa?

- A: Slovakia
- B: Paraguay
- C: New Zealand
- D: Cameroon

12

In which city was the final draw made for the 2010 World Cup?

- A: Cape Town
- B: Pretoria
- C: Johannesburg
- D: Durban

If you would like to use your 50:50 please turn to page 301
If you would like to use your Ask The Audience please turn to page 321
Turn to the answer section on page 333 to find out if you've won £4000!

7 ◆ £4000 WORLD CUP

13

In which of these years did England gain automatic qualification for the World Cup finals?

- A: 1970
- B: 1974
- C: 1978
- D: 1994

14

In 2014, which country will become only the fifth to stage the World Cup finals twice?

- A: Argentina
- B: Uruguay
- C: Brazil
- D: Chile

15

Which country hosted the World Cup finals for the second time in 1990?

- A: Italy
- B: Mexico
- C: Germany
- D: Spain

16

FIFA regulations for South Africa state squads may consist of a maximum of how many players?

- A: Thirty
- B: Twenty-seven
- C: Twenty-three
- D: Eighteen

If you would like to use your 50:50 please turn to page 301
If you would like to use your Ask The Audience please turn to page 321
Turn to the answer section on page 333 to find out if you've won £4000!

7 ◆ £4000 WORLD CUP

17

Morten Olsen was head coach of which team during their 2010 World Cup campaign?

- A: The Netherlands
- B: Switzerland
- C: Denmark
- D: Spain

18

Joachim Low was contracted to be head coach of which team during the 2010 World Cup?

- A: The Netherlands
- B: Germany
- C: Switzerland
- D: Spain

19

In which decade were The Netherlands twice World Cup finalists?

- A: 1950s
- B: 1960s
- C: 1970s
- D: 1980s

20

The Laudrup brothers represented which country in France in 1998?

- A: Norway
- B: Sweden
- C: Denmark
- D: Austria

If you would like to use your 50:50 please turn to page 301
If you would like to use your Ask The Audience please turn to page 321
Turn to the answer section on page 333 to find out if you've won £4000!

7 ◆ £4000 WORLD CUP

21

Which Spanish stadium was the venue for the 1982 World Cup final?

- A: Bernabéu
- B: Riazor
- C: Nou Camp
- D: Mestalla

22

Who recorded wins over Spain, Italy and Portugal on their way to the 2002 World Cup semis?

- A: Turkey
- B: Senegal
- C: USA
- D: South Korea

23

Nikola Zigic and Dejan Stankovic played for which team in the 2010 qualifying games?

- A: Slovakia
- B: Hungary
- C: Yugoslavia
- D: Serbia

24

Prior to 2010, which country's only appearance at the World Cup finals was in 1982?

- A: North Korea
- B: The Netherlands
- C: Nigeria
- D: New Zealand

If you would like to use your 50:50 please turn to page 301
If you would like to use your Ask The Audience please turn to page 321
Turn to the answer section on page 334 to find out if you've won £4000!

7 ◆ £4000 WORLD CUP

25

Which was the first South American team to qualify for South Africa?

- A: Chile
- B: Uruguay
- C: Paraguay
- D: Brazil

26

At the 2006 World Cup, what colour were Paraguay's first-choice shirts?

- A: Green
- B: Black and white stripe
- C: Red and white stripe
- D: Orange

27

Which 2010 qualifiers have red and white striped shirts as their first choice?

- A: Paraguay
- B: Cameroon
- C: Ghana
- D: North Korea

28

Where is the Loftus Versfeld stadium, one of those chosen for the 2010 World Cup finals?

- A: Pretoria
- B: Johannesburg
- C: Cape Town
- D: Durban

If you would like to use your 50:50 please turn to page 301
If you would like to use your Ask The Audience please turn to page 321
Turn to the answer section on page 334 to find out if you've won £4000!

7 ◆ £4000 WORLD CUP

29

Which other European country was grouped with England at the 2010 World Cup finals?

- A: Slovakia
- B: Greece
- C: Switzerland
- D: Slovenia

30

Who coached the Swiss national team during their 2010 campaign?

- A: Ottmar Hitzfeld
- B: Marcelo Bielsa
- C: Otto Rehhagel
- D: Morten Olsen

31

Tranquillo Barnetta is a key player in which 2010 qualifying side?

- A: Italy
- B: Switzerland
- C: Brazil
- D: Spain

32

Who was manager of Portugal during the 2010 World Cup finals?

- A: Luiz Felipe Scolari
- B: Humberto Coelho
- C: Carlos Queiros
- D: Agostinho Oliveira

If you would like to use your 50:50 please turn to page 301
If you would like to use your Ask The Audience please turn to page 321
Turn to the answer section on page 334 to find out if you've won £4000!

7 ◆ £4000 WORLD CUP

33

Which country did Nicklas Bendtner represent at the 2010 World Cup?

- A: Germany
- B: The Netherlands
- C: Denmark
- D: France

34

Which newcomer nation confounded expectations and finished third at the 1998 World Cup finals?

- A: Jamaica
- B: South Africa
- C: Croatia
- D: Japan

35

Which forward played in England's first three matches in the 1966 World Cup?

- A: Jeff Astle
- B: Jimmy Greaves
- C: Peter Osgood
- D: Johnny Haynes

36

Who was manager of the England team that ended the nation's twelve-year World Cup exile in 1982?

- A: Bobby Robson
- B: Ron Greenwood
- C: Sir Alf Ramsey
- D: Don Revie

If you would like to use your 50:50 please turn to page 301
If you would like to use your Ask The Audience please turn to page 321–322
Turn to the answer section on page 334 to find out if you've won £4000!

7 ◆ £4000 WORLD CUP

37

At the 2006 tournament, which country finished second behind England in the group stage?

- A: Trinidad & Tobago
- B: Sweden
- C: Paraguay
- D: Côte d'Ivoire

38

Which team lifted the World Cup trophy for the third time in 1990?

- A: Italy
- B: Argentina
- C: Brazil
- D: West Germany

39

Including 2010, how many times has the World Cup title been decided in the southern hemisphere?

- A: Five
- B: Six
- C: Seven
- D: Eight

40

Just north of which city is the Mbombela Stadium, a venue for the 2010 World Cup finals?

- A: Port Elizabeth
- B: Rustenburg
- C: Polokwane
- D: Nelspruit

If you would like to use your 50:50 please turn to page 301
If you would like to use your Ask The Audience please turn to page 322
Turn to the answer section on page 334 to find out if you've won £4000!

7 ◆ £4000 WORLD CUP

41

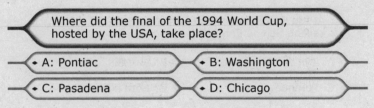

Where did the final of the 1994 World Cup, hosted by the USA, take place?

- A: Pontiac
- B: Washington
- C: Pasadena
- D: Chicago

If you would like to use your 50:50 please turn to page 301
If you would like to use your Ask The Audience please turn to page 322
Turn to the answer section on page 334 to find out if you've won £4000!

7 ◆ £4000 EUROPEAN

1

Libero is another term for what position on the field?

- A: Goalkeeper
- B: Striker
- C: Winger
- D: Sweeper

2

Which footballing legend named his son Jordi?

- A: Pelé
- B: Johan Cruyff
- C: Eusébio
- D: Diego Maradona

3

What became the home stadium of Juventus in 2006?

- A: San Siro
- B: Stadio Olimpico
- C: Luigi Ferraris
- D: Guissepe Meazza

4

What do the winners of Italy's Serie A receive?

- A: Trapetto
- B: Placca
- C: Scudetto
- D: Trofetto

If you would like to use your 50:50 please turn to page 301
If you would like to use your Ask The Audience please turn to page 322
Turn to the answer section on page 334 to find out if you've won £4000!

5

How many teams from the British Isles reached the finals of Euro 2008?

- A: None
- B: One
- C: Two
- D: Three

6

APOEL was the only club from which country in the group stages of the 2009/10 Champions League?

- A: Romania
- B: Bulgaria
- C: Cyprus
- D: Serbia

7

Which of these Dutch clubs is based in Amsterdam?

- A: Feyenoord
- B: NEC
- C: Ajax
- D: Vitesse

8

When the Allianz Arena in Munich hosts the German national team, by what colour light is it illuminated?

- A: Red
- B: White
- C: Blue
- D: Yellow

If you would like to use your 50:50 please turn to page 301
If you would like to use your Ask The Audience please turn to page 322
Turn to the answer section on page 334 to find out if you've won £4000!

7 ◆ £4000 EUROPEAN

9

Which German legend became the president of Bayern Munich in 1994?

- A: Franz Beckenbauer
- B: Gerd Müller
- C: Paul Breitner
- D: Lothar Matthäus

10

Which of these top-flight French clubs is not based on the mainland?

- A: FC Toulouse
- B: AC Ajaccio
- C: FA Nantes
- D: AJ Auxerre

11

What two digits follow FC Schalke to give the common name of a German Bundesliga club?

- A: 04
- B: 22
- C: 57
- D: 84

12

In the Europa League, how many teams qualify from the group stages for the next round?

- A: Eight
- B: Twelve
- C: Sixteen
- D: Twenty-four

If you would like to use your 50:50 please turn to page 301
If you would like to use your Ask The Audience please turn to page 322
Turn to the answer section on page 334 to find out if you've won £4000!

7 ◆ £4000 EUROPEAN

13

Magdeburg, the winners of the European Cup Winners' Cup in 1974, were from which country?

- A: Yugoslavia
- B: Czechoslovakia
- C: East Germany
- D: Soviet Union

14

Who won the European Cup three times as a player from 1971-73 and once as a manager in 1992?

- A: Frank de Boer
- B: Ruud Gullit
- C: Erwin Koeman
- D: Johan Cruyff

15

Who were the defeated finalists at Euro 2008?

- A: Croatia
- B: Italy
- C: Germany
- D: Portugal

16

In 1988, Guus Hiddink managed which team to the European Cup title?

- A: Porto
- B: PSV Eindhoven
- C: AC Milan
- D: Red Star Belgrade

If you would like to use your 50:50 please turn to page 301
If you would like to use your Ask The Audience please turn to page 322
Turn to the answer section on page 334 to find out if you've won £4000!

7 ◆ £4000 EUROPEAN

17

Which was the only Scandinavian team to win the UEFA Cup?

- A: Aalborg BK
- B: FC Lyn Oslo
- C: IFK Göteborg
- D: HJK Helsinki

18

The Allsvenskan is the top flight of domestic football in which country?

- A: Sweden
- B: Switzerland
- C: Serbia
- D: Slovenia

19

Who captained AC Milan to the Champions League title, forty years after his father did the same?

- A: Franco Baresi
- B: Paolo Maldini
- C: Roberto Baggio
- D: Roberto Donadoni

20

At which European Championship did a unified Germany team compete for the first time?

- A: 1980
- B: 1984
- C: 1988
- D: 1992

If you would like to use your 50:50 please turn to page 301
If you would like to use your Ask The Audience please turn to page 322
Turn to the answer section on page 334 to find out if you've won £4000!

7 ◆ £4000 DOMESTIC

1

The Arsenal manager Arsène Wenger has been nicknamed 'The . . .'?

- A: Doctor
- B: Boffin
- C: Teacher
- D: Professor

2

Which football manager sensationally left his club by mutual consent in September 2007?

- A: Steve Bruce
- B: Mark Hughes
- C: José Mourinho
- D: Harry Redknapp

3

A stand at Leicester City's Walkers Stadium was named after which local hero?

- A: Willie Thorne
- B: Alan Birchenhall
- C: Gary Lineker
- D: Frank Worthington

4

Which of these clubs is not nicknamed after a bird?

- A: Leicester City
- B: Newcastle United
- C: Norwich City
- D: Notts County

If you would like to use your 50:50 please turn to pages 301–302
If you would like to use your Ask The Audience please turn to page 322
Turn to the answer section on page 334 to find out if you've won £4000!

7 ◆ £4000 DOMESTIC

5

Which of these clubs did not play in a local derby league game in the 2009/10 season?

- A: Sunderland
- B: Everton
- C: Aston Villa
- D: Arsenal

6

Who is the Liverpool goalkeeper?

- A: Stephen Darby
- B: Emiliano Insua
- C: Nabil El Zhar
- D: Diego Cavalieri

7

John Madejski was appointed chairman of which club in 1990?

- A: Birmingham City
- B: Reading
- C: Leicester City
- D: Wycombe Wanderers

8

As of 2009, which club has won the FA Cup the most times?

- A: Chelsea
- B: Manchester United
- C: Tottenham Hotspur
- D: Blackburn Rovers

If you would like to use your 50:50 please turn to page 302
If you would like to use your Ask The Audience please turn to page 322
Turn to the answer section on page 334 to find out if you've won £4000!

7 ◆ £4000 DOMESTIC

9

Which of these is a former Scottish referee?

- A: Harry Detroit
- B: Hal Denver
- C: Hayden Delaware
- D: Hugh Dallas

10

Which team won the Championship play-offs at Wembley in May 2009?

- A: Sheffield United
- B: Burnley
- C: Reading
- D: Cardiff City

11

In May 2009, who did Chelsea beat 2-1 in the FA Cup final?

- A: Aston Villa
- B: Bolton Wanderers
- C: Manchester City
- D: Everton

12

Ian McParland was sacked as manager of which high-profile League Two club in October 2009?

- A: Chesterfield
- B: Burton Albion
- C: Notts County
- D: Lincoln City

If you would like to use your 50:50 please turn to page 302
If you would like to use your Ask The Audience please turn to page 322
Turn to the answer section on page 334 to find out if you've won £4000!

7 ◆ £4000 DOMESTIC

13

Which club signed the Russian striker Roman Pavlyuchenko for £14 million in 2008?

- A: Chelsea
- B: Tottenham Hotspur
- C: Liverpool
- D: Manchester City

14

Which club set a new British transfer record of £32.5 million in September 2008?

- A: Chelsea
- B: Manchester United
- C: Manchester City
- D: Everton

15

Which animal features on the badges of both Aston Villa and Middlesbrough?

- A: Eagle
- B: Horse
- C: Lion
- D: Cockerel

16

Blessed is the title of whose autobiography?

- A: Tony Adams
- B: Roy Keane
- C: George Best
- D: Nicky Butt

If you would like to use your 50:50 please turn to page 302
If you would like to use your Ask The Audience please turn to page 322
Turn to the answer section on page 334 to find out if you've won £4000!

7 ◆ £4000 DOMESTIC

17

Which of these is a Scottish league ground?

- A: Newel Park
- B: Banister Park
- C: Rise Park
- D: Stair Park

18

What is the nickname of Partick Thistle?

- A: The Rollers
- B: The Beamers
- C: The Jags
- D: The Mercs

19

Who is the only player to have scored in every season of the Premier League?

- A: Gary Neville
- B: Ryan Giggs
- C: Sol Campbell
- D: Dwight Yorke

20

Which of these does not appear on a list of players with 100 England caps?

- A: David Beckham
- B: Billy Wright
- C: Bobby Moore
- D: David Seaman

If you would like to use your 50:50 please turn to page 302
If you would like to use your Ask The Audience please turn to page 322
Turn to the answer section on page 334 to find out if you've won £4000!

50:50

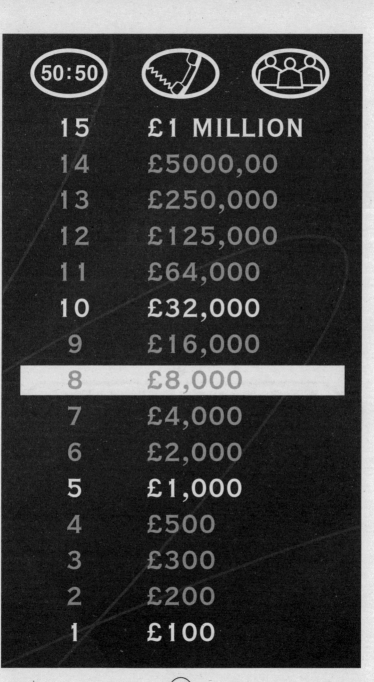

15	£1 MILLION
14	£5000,00
13	£250,000
12	£125,000
11	£64,000
10	£32,000
9	£16,000
8	£8,000
7	£4,000
6	£2,000
5	£1,000
4	£500
3	£300
2	£200
1	£100

8 ◆ £8000 WORLD CUP

1

What is the name of the stadium in Durban, chosen as an official venue for 2010?

- A: Coca-Cola Park
- B: Free State
- C: Green Point
- D: Moses Mabhida

2

Which of these Asian countries did not qualify for the 2010 World Cup finals?

- A: Japan
- B: China
- C: North Korea
- D: South Korea

3

What was the score after normal time in the 2006 final?

- A: 0-0
- B: 1-1
- C: 2-2
- D: 3-3

4

Who was the last man to coach Scotland at the World Cup finals?

- A: Andy Roxburgh
- B: Craig Brown
- C: Walter Smith
- D: Ally MacLeod

If you would like to use your 50:50 please turn to page 303
If you would like to use your Ask The Audience please turn to page 322
Turn to the answer section on page 334 to find out if you've won £8000!

8 ◆ £8000 WORLD CUP

5

At the 1998 tournament, all the surnames of which country's squad ended with a 'V'?

- A: Romania
- B: Bulgaria
- C: Russia
- D: Yugoslavia

6

What was unusual about the hat-trick scored by Laszlo Kiss in the 1982 tournament?

- A: All headers
- B: All offside
- C: He was a substitute
- D: All penalties

7

Which was the first World Cup finals to be broadcast on TV in colour?

- A: 1966
- B: 1970
- C: 1974
- D: 1978

8

What name was given to an infamous match between Italy and Chile in 1962?

- A: Battle of Milan
- B: Battle of Santiago
- C: Battle of Rome
- D: Battle of Talca

If you would like to use your 50:50 please turn to page 303
If you would like to use your Ask The Audience please turn to page 322
Turn to the answer section on page 334 to find out if you've won £8000!

8 ◆ £8000 WORLD CUP

9

Who won both their quarter and semi-final matches at the 1990 World Cup on penalty shoot-outs?

- A: Germany
- B: Italy
- C: England
- D: Argentina

10

Who did Portugal beat in a play-off to qualify for 2010?

- A: Estonia
- B: Armenia
- C: Belgium
- D: Bosnia-Herzegovina

11

Which was the first European country to host the World Cup finals?

- A: France
- B: Switzerland
- C: Sweden
- D: Italy

12

Which German player appeared in five consecutive World Cups between 1982 and 1998?

- A: Rudi Völler
- B: Jürgen Klinsmann
- C: Karlheinz Riedle
- D: Lothar Matthäus

If you would like to use your 50:50 please turn to page 303
If you would like to use your Ask The Audience please turn to page 322
Turn to the answer section on page 334 to find out if you've won £8000!

8 ◆ £8000 WORLD CUP

13

Which was the first World Cup final to produce less than three goals?

- A: 1990
- B: 1994
- C: 1998
- D: 2002

14

A small cowboy called Gauchito was the mascot for which tournament?

- A: Argentina, 1978
- B: Spain, 1982
- C: Mexico, 1986
- D: Italy, 1990

15

How is the Brazilian-born footballer Anderson Luís de Souza commonly known?

- A: Kaká
- B: Dunga
- C: Lúcio
- D: Deco

16

In which city is the Royal Bafokeng Sports Palace a designated stadium for the 2010 World Cup?

- A: Polokwane
- B: Nelspruit
- C: Pretoria
- D: Rustenburg

If you would like to use your 50:50 please turn to page 303
If you would like to use your Ask The Audience please turn to page 322
Turn to the answer section on page 334 to find out if you've won £8000!

8 ◆ £8000 WORLD CUP

17

Which country lost both the World Cup finals held in the 1980s?

- A: West Germany
- B: The Netherlands
- C: Argentina
- D: Italy

18

Who qualified for the 2010 World Cup finals over three months before any other European team?

- A: England
- B: Germany
- C: Denmark
- D: The Netherlands

19

In which two years did the World Cup mascots wear sombreros?

- A: 1974 and 1982
- B: 1970 and 1986
- C: 1978 and 2002
- D: 1966 and 1994

20

Which country ended Japan's run in the 2002 World Cup by beating them 1-0 in the second round?

- A: Germany
- B: Turkey
- C: Senegal
- D: Spain

If you would like to use your 50:50 please turn to page 303
If you would like to use your Ask The Audience please turn to page 322
Turn to the answer section on page 334 to find out if you've won £8000!

8 ◆ £8000 WORLD CUP

21

Which is the only country to have held a World Cup final in two different cities?

- A: Mexico
- B: Germany
- C: Italy
- D: France

22

How many nations participated in the qualifying rounds of the 2010 World Cup?

- A: 104
- B: 144
- C: 200
- D: 244

23

In which year was the World Cup final played in the city of Montevideo?

- A: 1958
- B: 1954
- C: 1934
- D: 1930

24

Whose number 10 shirt worn in the 1970 World Cup fetched a record £157,750 at a 2002 auction?

- A: Pelé
- B: Bobby Charlton
- C: Gerd Müller
- D: Johan Cruyff

If you would like to use your 50:50 please turn to page 303
If you would like to use your Ask The Audience please turn to page 323
Turn to the answer section on page 334 to find out if you've won £8000!

8 ◆ £8000 WORLD CUP

25

In which year did Northern Ireland last qualify for the World Cup?

- A: 1974
- B: 1978
- C: 1982
- D: 1986

26

Which country finished third at the 2002 World Cup?

- A: South Korea
- B: Turkey
- C: Japan
- D: Senegal

27

Which of these England players made his World Cup debut in 2002?

- A: David Beckham
- B: Michael Owen
- C: John Terry
- D: Wayne Bridge

28

Which World Cup hosts chose Pique the Chili Pepper as their mascot for the tournament?

- A: Spain
- B: Italy
- C: Argentina
- D: Mexico

If you would like to use your 50:50 please turn to page 303
If you would like to use your Ask The Audience please turn to page 323
Turn to the answer section on page 334 to find out if you've won £8000!

8 ◆ £8000 WORLD CUP

29

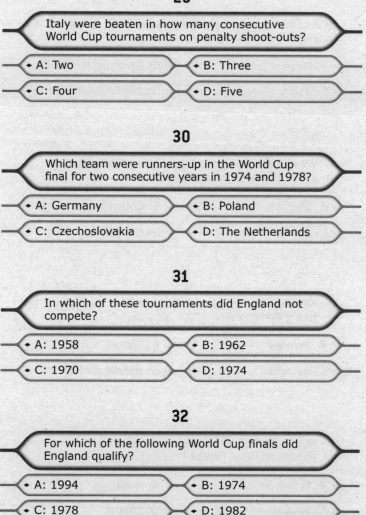

Italy were beaten in how many consecutive World Cup tournaments on penalty shoot-outs?

- A: Two
- B: Three
- C: Four
- D: Five

30

Which team were runners-up in the World Cup final for two consecutive years in 1974 and 1978?

- A: Germany
- B: Poland
- C: Czechoslovakia
- D: The Netherlands

31

In which of these tournaments did England not compete?

- A: 1958
- B: 1962
- C: 1970
- D: 1974

32

For which of the following World Cup finals did England qualify?

- A: 1994
- B: 1974
- C: 1978
- D: 1982

If you would like to use your 50:50 please turn to page 303
If you would like to use your Ask The Audience please turn to page 323
Turn to the answer section on page 334 to find out if you've won £8000!

8 ◆ £8000 WORLD CUP

33

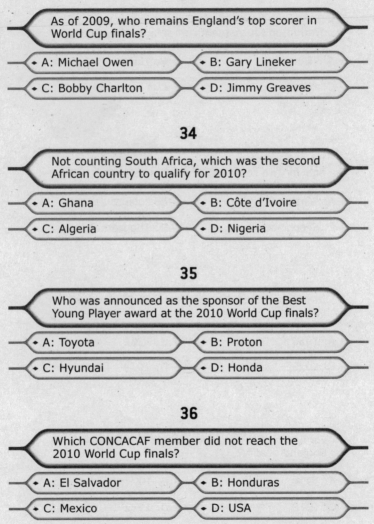

As of 2009, who remains England's top scorer in World Cup finals?

- A: Michael Owen
- B: Gary Lineker
- C: Bobby Charlton
- D: Jimmy Greaves

34

Not counting South Africa, which was the second African country to qualify for 2010?

- A: Ghana
- B: Côte d'Ivoire
- C: Algeria
- D: Nigeria

35

Who was announced as the sponsor of the Best Young Player award at the 2010 World Cup finals?

- A: Toyota
- B: Proton
- C: Hyundai
- D: Honda

36

Which CONCACAF member did not reach the 2010 World Cup finals?

- A: El Salvador
- B: Honduras
- C: Mexico
- D: USA

If you would like to use your 50:50 please turn to page 303
If you would like to use your Ask The Audience please turn to page 323
Turn to the answer section on page 334 to find out if you've won £8000!

8 ◆ £8000 WORLD CUP

37

Of the eighteen World Cup finals prior to 2010, how many have been won by European teams?

- A: Seven
- B: Eight
- C: Nine
- D: Ten

38

Which of these 2010 venues is in Pretoria?

- A: Green Point
- B: Loftus Versfeld
- C: Free State
- D: Soccer City

If you would like to use your 50:50 please turn to page 303
If you would like to use your Ask The Audience please turn to page 323
Turn to the answer section on page 334 to find out if you've won £8000!

8 ◆ £8000 EUROPEAN

1

What was the role of the Italian Roberto Rosetti in the final of Euro 2008?

- A: Referee
- B: Presented the cup
- C: Sang the anthems
- D: Stadium doctor

2

The finals of Euro 2016 will be expanded to include how many qualifying teams plus the hosts?

- A: Sixteen
- B: Twenty-four
- C: Thirty-two
- D: Forty-eight

3

Which is the only country to have been disqualified from entering the European Championship?

- A: East Germany
- B: Yugoslavia
- C: Spain
- D: Wales

4

Which German team has yet to win the European Cup or Champions League?

- A: Bayer Leverkusen
- B: Bayern Munich
- C: Hamburg
- D: Borussia Dortmund

If you would like to use your 50:50 please turn to page 303
If you would like to use your Ask The Audience please turn to page 323
Turn to the answer section on page 334 to find out if you've won £8000!

8 ◆ £8000 EUROPEAN

5

Denmark's national football team is nicknamed 'Danish . . .'?

- A: Devils
- B: Dragons
- C: Dynamite
- D: Dynamo

6

In 1985, Videoton reached the UEFA Cup final – in which country is this club based?

- A: Hungary
- B: Finland
- C: Greece
- D: Switzerland

7

Which was the first club to take the European Cup behind the Iron Curtain?

- A: Steaua Bucharest
- B: Dynamo Tbilisi
- C: Red Star Belgrade
- D: Shakhtar Donetsk

8

With a total of six, what club had most players on the shortlist for the 2009 World Player?

- A: Barcelona
- B: Real Madrid
- C: Atlético Madrid
- D: AC Milan

If you would like to use your 50:50 please turn to page 303
If you would like to use your Ask The Audience please turn to page 323
Turn to the answer section on page 334 to find out if you've won £8000!

8 ◆ £8000 EUROPEAN

9

Which team did Ljupko Petrovic coach to winning the European Cup?

- A: Red Star Belgrade
- B: Steaua Bucharest
- C: Dynamo Kiev
- D: Magdeburg

10

Which country were defeated twice by Greece in the finals of Euro 2004?

- A: France
- B: Portugal
- C: Czech Republic
- D: Russia

11

In 1960/61, which team broke Real Madrid's run of five consecutive European Cup titles?

- A: AC Milan
- B: Benfica
- C: Eintracht Frankfurt
- D: Barcelona

12

Who is The Netherlands' most capped player?

- A: Frank de Boer
- B: Phillip Cocu
- C: Edwin van der Sar
- D: Marco van Basten

If you would like to use your 50:50 please turn to page 303
If you would like to use your Ask The Audience please turn to page 323
Turn to the answer section on page 334 to find out if you've won £8000!

8 ◆ £8000 EUROPEAN

13

Who was appointed manager of Barcelona in 2008?

- A: Pep Guardiola
- B: Manuel Pellegrini
- C: Javier Aguirre
- D: Joaquín Caparrós

14

Which country's national team was known in the 1950s as the 'Magical Magyars'?

- A: Poland
- B: Hungary
- C: Romania
- D: Bulgaria

15

Which country's Under-21 team is known as the 'Azzurrini'?

- A: Italy
- B: Portugal
- C: France
- D: Spain

16

Which Italian club did Sven-Göran Eriksson leave to become England manager?

- A: Inter Milan
- B: Roma
- C: Juventus
- D: Lazio

If you would like to use your 50:50 please turn to page 303
If you would like to use your Ask The Audience please turn to page 323
Turn to the answer section on page 334 to find out if you've won £8000!

8 ◆ £8000 EUROPEAN

17

What is a popular name given to German clubs from the former Kingdom of Prussia?

- A: Bayern
- B: Borussia
- C: Werder
- D: Hertha

18

Which of these 2009/10 Dutch Eredivisie clubs shares its name with a mythological hero?

- A: Achilles
- B: Heracles
- C: Perseus
- D: Odysseus

19

Which country entered Euro 2004 as reigning champions?

- A: Italy
- B: Germany
- C: France
- D: Spain

If you would like to use your 50:50 please turn to page 303
If you would like to use your Ask The Audience please turn to page 323
Turn to the answer section on page 334 to find out if you've won £8000!

8 ◆ £8000 DOMESTIC

1

How many teams comprised the Scottish Premier League in the 2009/10 season?

- A: Eight
- B: Ten
- C: Twelve
- D: Fourteen

2

Mother Noblett's Toffee Shop used to be near which football ground?

- A: Craven Cottage
- B: Goodison Park
- C: St Andrews
- D: Elland Road

3

In 1970, which club beat Leeds United 2-1 to win the first-ever replayed FA Cup final?

- A: Arsenal
- B: Liverpool
- C: Manchester City
- D: Chelsea

4

Which tree forms part of the name of Barnsley's home ground?

- A: Yew
- B: Ash
- C: Elm
- D: Oak

If you would like to use your 50:50 please turn to page 303
If you would like to use your Ask The Audience please turn to page 323
Turn to the answer section on page 335 to find out if you've won £8000!

5

Sheikh Mansour bin Zayed Al Nayan is the owner of which club?

- A: Manchester City
- B: Everton
- C: Rangers
- D: Tottenham Hotspur

6

Whose number for international caps did David Beckham equal in February 2009?

- A: Bobby Charlton
- B: Bobby Moore
- C: Peter Shilton
- D: Billy Wright

7

Which Scottish league club is nicknamed 'The Bairns'?

- A: Dundee United
- B: Dunfermline
- C: Aberdeen
- D: Falkirk

8

What is the first name of the player Boateng, signed by Portsmouth in the 2009/10 season?

- A: Ellis-Duke
- B: Kevin-Prince
- C: Roy-King
- D: Larry-Earl

If you would like to use your 50:50 please turn to pages 303–304
If you would like to use your Ask The Audience please turn to page 323
Turn to the answer section on page 335 to find out if you've won £8000!

8 ◆ £8000 DOMESTIC

9

Who were England's opponents in the world's first international match played in 1872?

- A: France
- B: Ireland
- C: Scotland
- D: Wales

10

Which of these has never won the BBC Sports Personality of the Year Award?

- A: Bobby Moore
- B: Gary Lineker
- C: Michael Owen
- D: David Beckham

11

In 2007, a company led by the former prime minister of Thailand bought which English club?

- A: Newcastle United
- B: Sunderland
- C: Fulham
- D: Manchester City

12

In which city are the Ashton Gate and the Memorial Stadium grounds?

- A: Nottingham
- B: Bristol
- C: Sheffield
- D: Birmingham

If you would like to use your 50:50 please turn to page 304
If you would like to use your Ask The Audience please turn to page 323
Turn to the answer section on page 335 to find out if you've won £8000!

8 ◆ £8000 DOMESTIC

13

Who sponsored the Scottish Premier League for the 2009/10 season?

- A: Arnold Clark
- B: RBS
- C: Famous Grouse
- D: Clydesdale Bank

14

A statue of which former Leeds United player stands outside Elland Road?

- A: Jack Charlton
- B: Johnny Giles
- C: Gary Sprake
- D: Billy Bremner

15

South Africa Road in London is the address of which club's home ground?

- A: Fulham
- B: QPR
- C: Brentford
- D: Leyton Orient

16

Which of these is a top-flight Welsh league club?

- A: Dragon Air Houghton
- B: Airbus UK Broughton
- C: Air Wales Loughton
- D: Jumbo Jet Stoughton

If you would like to use your 50:50 please turn to page 304
If you would like to use your Ask The Audience please turn to page 323
Turn to the answer section on page 335 to find out if you've won £8000!

8 ◆ £8000 DOMESTIC

17

Through The Wind And Rain is a long-running fanzine of which club?

- A: Newcastle United
- B: Sunderland
- C: Liverpool
- D: Middlesbrough

18

Which member of the Royal Family was president of the FA from 2000-06?

- A: Duke of Gloucester
- B: Duke of York
- C: Duke of Kent
- D: Duke of Edinburgh

19

Which is Scotland's oldest football club, founded in 1867?

- A: Celtic
- B: Queen's Park
- C: Queen of the South
- D: Rangers

If you would like to use your 50:50 please turn to page 304
If you would like to use your Ask The Audience please turn to page 323
Turn to the answer section on page 335 to find out if you've won £8000!

50:50

15	£1 MILLION
14	£5000,00
13	£250,000
12	£125,000
11	£64,000
10	£32,000
9	£16,000
8	£8,000
7	£4,000
6	£2,000
5	£1,000
4	£500
3	£300
2	£200
1	£100

9 ◆ £16,000 WORLD CUP

1

Which side did Slovenia defeat in the play-offs in order to qualify for South Africa?

- A: Ukraine
- B: Greece
- C: Republic of Ireland
- D: Russia

2

Which team scored the greatest number of goals, a total of fourteen, at the 2006 World Cup finals?

- A: Argentina
- B: Brazil
- C: Italy
- D: Germany

3

At the time of the 2006 World Cup finals, Germany's Robert Huth was signed to which club?

- A: Chelsea
- B: Aston Villa
- C: Arsenal
- D: Manchester City

4

Which World Cup tournament was the first to involve British players?

- A:1934
- B:1938
- C:1950
- D:1954

If you would like to use your 50:50 please turn to page 305
If you would like to use your Ask The Audience please turn to page 323
Turn to the answer section on page 335 to find out if you've won £16,000!

9 ◆ £16,000 WORLD CUP

5

In 2006, who became the highest goalscorer in the history of the World Cup finals?

- A: Ronaldo
- B: Paolo Maldini
- C: Cristiano Ronaldo
- D: Kaká

6

England was in which European qualifying group for the 2010 World Cup finals?

- A: Four
- B: Five
- C: Six
- D: Seven

7

How many European qualifying groups were there for the 2010 World Cup finals?

- A: Nine
- B: Ten
- C: Eleven
- D: Twelve

8

Who defeated El Salvador by a record score of 10-1 at the 1982 tournament?

- A: Hungary
- B: Brazil
- C: West Germany
- D: The Netherlands

If you would like to use your 50:50 please turn to page 305
If you would like to use your Ask The Audience please turn to page 323
Turn to the answer section on page 335 to find out if you've won £16,000!

9 ◆ £16,000 WORLD CUP

9

Which of these former countries made its only appearance at the World Cup finals in 1974?

- A: South Vietnam
- B: East Germany
- C: Czechoslovakia
- D: Yugoslavia

10

In 1986, which of these countries made its World Cup finals debut?

- A: Denmark
- B: Sweden
- C: Norway
- D: Finland

11

In which year did Scotland make its World Cup finals debut?

- A: 1954
- B: 1962
- C: 1966
- D: 1970

12

Which Italian won both the Golden Ball and the Golden Shoe Awards at the 1990 World Cup finals?

- A: Carlo Ancelotti
- B: Roberto Baggio
- C: Salvatore Schillaci
- D: Gianluca Vialli

If you would like to use your 50:50 please turn to page 305
If you would like to use your Ask The Audience please turn to page 323–324
Turn to the answer section on page 335 to find out if you've won £16,000!

9 ◆ £16,000 WORLD CUP

13

Who beat the defending champions France in the opening match of the 2002 World Cup finals?

- A: Uruguay
- B: Denmark
- C: Senegal
- D: Costa Rica

14

How many teams qualified automatically for the 2002 World Cup finals?

- A: One
- B: Two
- C: Three
- D: None

15

The oldest player to score a World Cup finals goal is Roger Milla – who did he play for?

- A: Jamaica
- B: Togo
- C: Cameroon
- D: Nigeria

16

How many teams qualified directly for the 2010 World Cup finals from CONMEBOL?

- A: Six
- B: Five
- C: Four
- D: Three

If you would like to use your 50:50 please turn to page 305
If you would like to use your Ask The Audience please turn to page 324
Turn to the answer section on page 335 to find out if you've won £16,000!

9 ◆ £16,000 WORLD CUP

17

Of all the former champions, which were the last two to qualify for the 2010 World Cup finals?

- A: France and Uruguay
- B: Italy and England
- C: Germany and Brazil
- D: Argentina and Italy

18

Which was the last World Cup finals in which Germany did not compete?

- A: 1934
- B: 1938
- C: 1950
- D: 1958

19

At which World Cup finals did Croatia make their debut?

- A: 1990
- B: 1994
- C: 1998
- D: 2002

20

The stadium at Vodacom Park, a venue chosen for the 2010 World Cup finals, is known by what other name?

- A: Eastern Cape Stadium
- B: Free State Stadium
- C: Limpopo Stadium
- D: KwaZulu-Natal Stadium

If you would like to use your 50:50 please turn to page 305
If you would like to use your Ask The Audience please turn to page 324
Turn to the answer section on page 335 to find out if you've won £16,000!

9 ◆ £16,000 WORLD CUP

21

Which is the most westerly city to have hosted a World Cup final?

- A: Santiago
- B: Montevideo
- C: Pasadena
- D: Mexico City

22

Seen at the 2010 World Cup finals, a Jabulani is what?

- A: War dance
- B: Official match ball
- C: Tournament mascot
- D: Ambulance

23

What is the longest period between Brazil lifting the World Cup?

- A: Twelve years
- B: Sixteen years
- C: Twenty years
- D: Twenty-four years

24

To 2010, with whom does Peter Shilton share the record of ten clean sheets in World Cup finals?

- A: Oliver Kahn
- B: Fabien Barthez
- C: Michel Preud'homme
- D: Gianluigi Buffon

If you would like to use your 50:50 please turn to page 305
If you would like to use your Ask The Audience please turn to page 324
Turn to the answer section on page 335 to find out if you've won £16,000!

9 ◆ £16,000 WORLD CUP

25

Which member of the German 2010 qualifying squad has been dubbed the 'Little Kaiser'?

- A: Lukas Podolski
- B: Philipp Lahm
- C: Michael Ballack
- D: Andreas Beck

26

Guillermo Stábile of Argentina was the top scorer at which World Cup tournament?

- A: 1930, Uruguay
- B: 1950, Brazil
- C: 1966, England
- D: 2006, Germany

27

Which of these European teams did not play in the first World Cup tournament?

- A: France
- B: Yugoslavia
- C: Italy
- D: Belgium

28

Which England player holds the record for most World Cup finals matches played - a total of seventeen?

- A: Peter Shilton
- B: Terry Butcher
- C: David Beckham
- D: Bobby Charlton

If you would like to use your 50:50 please turn to page 305
If you would like to use your Ask The Audience please turn to page 324
Turn to the answer section on page 335 to find out if you've won £16,000!

9 ◆ £16,000 WORLD CUP

29

Which European country was grouped with ex-champions Argentina at the 2010 World Cup finals?

- A: Greece
- B: Switzerland
- C: Slovakia
- D: Denmark

30

Prior to 2010, which country's only appearance at the World Cup finals was in 2006?

- A: Greece
- B: Honduras
- C: Côte d'Ivoire
- D: Australia

31

Mourad Meghni, nicknamed 'Le Petit Zidane', helped which country qualify for South Africa?

- A: France
- B: Côte d'Ivoire
- C: Algeria
- D: Cameroon

32

Which country played the most qualifying games to reach South Africa 2010?

- A: Chile
- B: Paraguay
- C: Honduras
- D: Uruguay

If you would like to use your 50:50 please turn to page 305
If you would like to use your Ask The Audience please turn to page 324
Turn to the answer section on page 335 to find out if you've won £16,000!

9 ◆ £16,000 WORLD CUP

33

Which of these teams has appeared in the most World Cup tournaments?

- A: Argentina
- B: Italy
- C: England
- D: Spain

34

In which group were Spain, the highest-ranked team in the 2010 tournament, drawn?

- A: E
- B: F
- C: G
- D: H

35

Which national side are commonly known as 'A Seleção', meaning 'The selection'?

- A: Portugal
- B: Spain
- C: Brazil
- D: Mexico

36

Which year marked England's debut in the World Cup finals?

- A:1934
- B:1938
- C:1950
- D:1954

If you would like to use your 50:50 please turn to page 305
If you would like to use your Ask The Audience please turn to page 324
Turn to the answer section on page 335 to find out if you've won £16,000!

9 ◆ £16,000 EUROPEAN

1

How many handles does the UEFA Super Cup have?

- A: None
- B: Two
- C: Three
- D: Four

2

Which is the only Belgian team to have reached the European Cup final?

- A: Anderlecht
- B: Bruges
- C: Standard Liège
- D: Mechelen

3

Who did Liverpool beat in the 2001 UEFA Cup final, the first to be decided by a golden goal?

- A: Lazio
- B: Espanyol
- C: Marseille
- D: Alavés

4

What is the goalkeeper Jens Lehmann's claim to fame in Champions League final history?

- A: First keeper to score
- B: Played in glasses
- C: Punched the referee
- D: First-ever red card

If you would like to use your 50:50 please turn to page 305
If you would like to use your Ask The Audience please turn to page 324
Turn to the answer section on page 335 to find out if you've won £16,000!

9 ◆ £16,000 EUROPEAN

5

Prior to 2010, which is the only Greek team to make the European Cup or Champions League final?

- A: AEK Athens
- B: PAOK
- C: Panathinaikos
- D: Olympiacos

6

Who won a European Cup winners' medal with both Manchester United and Aston Villa?

- A: John Aston
- B: Shay Brennan
- C: Jimmy Rimmer
- D: Gordon Cowans

7

Who is the only Scottish manager to have won the UEFA Cup?

- A: Alex Ferguson
- B: Jock Stein
- C: Bill Shankly
- D: Walter Smith

8

As of January 2010, who has scored the most goals in the Champions League?

- A: Andriy Shevchenko
- B: Thierry Henry
- C: Filippo Inzaghi
- D: Raúl

If you would like to use your 50:50 please turn to page 305
If you would like to use your Ask The Audience please turn to page 324
Turn to the answer section on page 335 to find out if you've won £16,000!

9 ◆ £16,000 EUROPEAN

9

Since the European Cup became the Champions League, who has won it the most times?

- A: Juventus
- B: Porto
- C: Liverpool
- D: AC Milan

10

Which English club was on the wrong end of a 4-0 score line in the 2006 UEFA Cup final?

- A: Aston Villa
- B: Middlesbrough
- C: Everton
- D: Tottenham Hotspur

11

Which was the only Croatian club in the group stages of the 2009/10 Europa League?

- A: HNK Cibalia
- B: NK Osijek
- C: HNK Hajduk Split
- D: NK Dinamo Zagreb

12

FK Ventspils, a team in the group stages of the 2009/10 Europa League, is from which country?

- A: Moldova
- B: Croatia
- C: Latvia
- D: Belarus

If you would like to use your 50:50 please turn to page 305
If you would like to use your Ask The Audience please turn to page 324
Turn to the answer section on page 335 to find out if you've won £16,000!

9 ◆ £16,000 EUROPEAN

13

Hans Krankl played for, and later managed, which national team?

- A: Germany
- B: Poland
- C: Austria
- D: Switzerland

14

In February 2008, Marco Tardelli was appointed assistant manager of which national team?

- A: Republic of Ireland
- B: Spain
- C: Italy
- D: Sweden

15

Which two Dutch teams take part in The National Derby or De Klassieker?

- A: Feyenoord and PSV
- B: Ajax and Feyenoord
- C: Vitesse and Groningen
- D: PSV and Ajax

16

In which city is Juventus based?

- A: Genoa
- B: Turin
- C: Rome
- D: Florence

If you would like to use your 50:50 please turn to page 305
If you would like to use your Ask The Audience please turn to page 324
Turn to the answer section on page 335 to find out if you've won £16,000!

9 ◆ £16,000 EUROPEAN

17

To April 2010, which is the only French team to have won the Champions League or its predecessor?

- A: Lyon
- B: Paris Saint-Germain
- C: Auxerre
- D: Marseille

18

Who won European Cup and Champions League winners' medals in 1989, 1990, 1994, 2003 and 2007?

- A: Filippo Inzaghi
- B: Giuseppe Favalli
- C: Paolo Maldini
- D: Massimo Oddo

If you would like to use your 50:50 please turn to page 305
If you would like to use your Ask The Audience please turn to page 324
Turn to the answer section on page 335 to find out if you've won £16,000!

9 ◆ £16,000 DOMESTIC

1

What nationality is Manchester United's Nemanja Vidic?

- A: Serbian
- B: Slovakian
- C: Slovenian
- D: Swiss

2

The Chelsea centre back Jeffrey Bruma is originally from which country?

- A: USA
- B: Australia
- C: The Netherlands
- D: Swaziland

3

If the 2009/10 Premier League ended alphabetically how many London teams would be in the top six?

- A: One
- B: Two
- C: Three
- D: Four

4

Who was Manchester United's longest-serving captain, holding the job for twelve years?

- A: Roy Keane
- B: Martin Buchan
- C: Bobby Charlton
- D: Bryan Robson

If you would like to use your 50:50 please turn to page 305
If you would like to use your Ask The Audience please turn to page 324
Turn to the answer section on page 335 to find out if you've won £16,000!

9 ◆ £16,000 DOMESTIC

5

What is the name of Arsenal's mascot?

- A: Arsenoraptor
- B: Gunnersaurus Rex
- C: Emiratodon
- D: Wengerdocus

6

Where did Eric Cantona launch his infamous kung fu kick at a supporter?

- A: Villa Park
- B: Selhurst Park
- C: Highbury
- D: Stamford Bridge

7

Which former Liverpool player designed the Predator football boot?

- A: Sammy Lee
- B: Jimmy Case
- C: Mark Lawrenson
- D: Craig Johnston

8

Who was the first non-British manager to win the Premier League?

- A: José Mourinho
- B: Rafael Benitez
- C: Arsène Wenger
- D: Claudio Ranieri

If you would like to use your 50:50 please turn to page 305
If you would like to use your Ask The Audience please turn to page 324
Turn to the answer section on page 335 to find out if you've won £16,000!

9 ◆ £16,000 DOMESTIC

9

In May 2009, who did Rangers beat 1-0 in the Scottish FA Cup final?

- A: Falkirk
- B: St Mirren
- C: Aberdeen
- D: Dundee United

10

In September 2009, who left his new club after playing only one game?

- A: Darren Bent
- B: Rory Delap
- C: Sol Campbell
- D: Greg Halford

11

Which club plays home games at Griffin Park?

- A: Southend United
- B: Brentford
- C: Tranmere Rovers
- D: Port Vale

12

4000 Holes is a fanzine dedicated to which Lancashire club?

- A: Preston North End
- B: Blackpool
- C: Burnley
- D: Blackburn Rovers

If you would like to use your 50:50 please turn to page 306
If you would like to use your Ask The Audience please turn to page 324
Turn to the answer section on page 335 to find out if you've won £16,000!

9 ◆ £16,000 DOMESTIC

13

Which former Chelsea player was appointed as manager at West Bromwich Albion in June 2009?

- A: Kerry Dixon
- B: Eddie Newton
- C: Gianfranco Zola
- D: Roberto Di Matteo

14

In May 2009, 'Mixu' Paatelainen resigned as manager of which Scottish club?

- A: Rangers
- B: Aberdeen
- C: Kilmarnock
- D: Hibernian

15

12 Albion Place in Edinburgh is the address of which club's home ground?

- A: Hibernian
- B: Heart of Midlothian
- C: Queen of the South
- D: Queens Park

16

Which club lost its league status in 2008?

- A: Brentford
- B: Chester City
- C: Grimsby Town
- D: Mansfield Town

If you would like to use your 50:50 please turn to page 306
If you would like to use your Ask The Audience please turn to page 324
Turn to the answer section on page 335 to find out if you've won £16,000!

9 ◆ £16,000 DOMESTIC

17

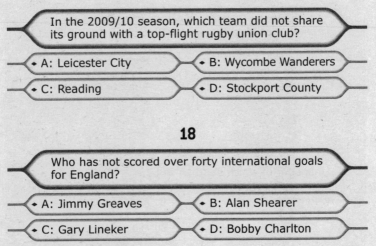

In the 2009/10 season, which team did not share its ground with a top-flight rugby union club?

- A: Leicester City
- B: Wycombe Wanderers
- C: Reading
- D: Stockport County

18

Who has not scored over forty international goals for England?

- A: Jimmy Greaves
- B: Alan Shearer
- C: Gary Lineker
- D: Bobby Charlton

If you would like to use your 50:50 please turn to page 306
If you would like to use your Ask The Audience please turn to page 324
Turn to the answer section on page 335 to find out if you've won £16,000!

50:50

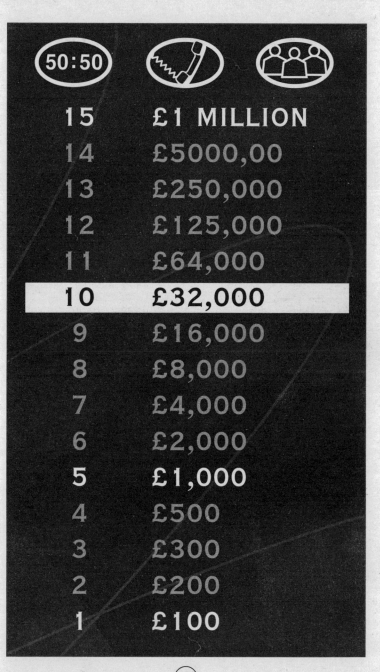

15	£1 MILLION
14	£5000,00
13	£250,000
12	£125,000
11	£64,000
10	£32,000
9	£16,000
8	£8,000
7	£4,000
6	£2,000
5	£1,000
4	£500
3	£300
2	£200
1	£100

10 ◆ £32,000 WORLD CUP

1

To 2010, which Middle Eastern country's only appearance at the World Cup finals was in 1982?

- A: Bahrain
- B: Qatar
- C: Kuwait
- D: Saudi Arabia

2

Which was the first World Cup tournament to be televised?

- A: 1938
- B: 1950
- C: 1954
- D: 1958

3

Prior to winning in 1998, how many times had France finished runners-up in the World Cup?

- A: Never
- B: Once
- C: Twice
- D: Three

4

Lukas Podolski, voted the Best Young Player at the 2006 tournament, represented which country?

- A: Poland
- B: Ukraine
- C: Italy
- D: Germany

If you would like to use your 50:50 please turn to page 307
If you would like to use your Ask The Audience please turn to page 324
Turn to the answer section on page 335 to find out if you've won £32,000!

10 ◆ £32,000 WORLD CUP

5

What does the second 'C' stand for in the name of the confederation CONCACAF?

- A: Caribbean
- B: Central
- C: Canadian
- D: Continent

6

Which team lost on penalties in the quarter-finals of both the 1986 and 2002 World Cup finals?

- A: England
- B: Spain
- C: France
- D: The Netherlands

7

Ricki Herbert was head coach of which team during their 2010 World Cup campaign?

- A: Mexico
- B: USA
- C: Australia
- D: New Zealand

8

In which two years have the official World Cup mascots been lions?

- A: 1966 and 1994
- B: 1966 and 1998
- C: 1966 and 2002
- D: 1966 and 2006

If you would like to use your 50:50 please turn to page 307
If you would like to use your Ask The Audience please turn to page 324–325
Turn to the answer section on page 335 to find out if you've won £32,000!

10 ◆ £32,000 WORLD CUP

9

At the 1990 World Cup finals, what did the UAE players receive for every goal they scored?

- A: $1,000,000
- B: A private jet
- C: A luxury yacht
- D: A Rolls-Royce

10

Following Pelé's retirement, who wore the number 10 shirt for Brazil at the 1974 World Cup finals?

- A: Rivelino
- B: Paulo Cesar
- C: Alfredo
- D: Jairzinho

11

Prior to 2010, which country's only appearance at the World Cup finals was in 1982?

- A: Chile
- B: Honduras
- C: Paraguay
- D: Nigeria

12

Prior to 2010, in which World Cup tournament did North Korea last meet Portugal?

- A: 1966
- B: 1970
- C: 1978
- D: 1986

If you would like to use your 50:50 please turn to page 307
If you would like to use your Ask The Audience please turn to page 325
Turn to the answer section on page 335 to find out if you've won £32,000!

10 ◆ £32,000 WORLD CUP

13

Diego Forlán was which country's top scorer in their 2010 World Cup qualifying campaign?

- A: Argentina
- B: Chile
- C: Uruguay
- D: Mexico

14

Which of these 2010 World Cup finals stadia is the highest above sea level?

- A: Green Point
- B: Moses Mabhida
- C: Nelson Mandela Bay
- D: Soccer City

15

In which group were the reigning champions, Italy, drawn for the 2010 World Cup finals?

- A: E
- B: F
- C: G
- D: H

16

Which of these non-national capital cities has hosted a World Cup final?

- A: New York
- B: Yokohama
- C: Milan
- D: Barcelona

If you would like to use your 50:50 please turn to page 307
If you would like to use your Ask The Audience please turn to page 325
Turn to the answer section on pages 335–336 to find out if you've won £32,000!

10 ◆ £32,000 WORLD CUP

17

Prior to 2014, which country's only appearance in a World Cup final was in 1958?

- A: Austria
- B: Sweden
- C: Bulgaria
- D: Chile

18

Who won the Golden Shoe award at the 1970 World Cup finals?

- A: Pelé
- B: Gerd Müller
- C: Jairzinho
- D: Gianni Rivera

19

Which country was chosen to host the 2011 Women's World Cup?

- A: Egypt
- B: Mexico
- C: Germany
- D: India

20

Vladimir Weiss was head coach of which team during their 2010 World Cup campaign?

- A: Serbia
- B: Germany
- C: Switzerland
- D: Slovakia

If you would like to use your 50:50 please turn to page 307
If you would like to use your Ask The Audience please turn to page 325
Turn to the answer section on page 336 to find out if you've won £32,000!

10 ◆ £32,000 WORLD CUP

21

Which of these 2010 qualifiers is sometimes nicknamed 'The Pirate Ship'?

- A: Honduras
- B: Greece
- C: Ghana
- D: Spain

22

Which World Cup-winning team has reached the finals of the World Cup the least number of times?

- A: France
- B: England
- C: Argentina
- D: Uruguay

23

Which of these has not captained Germany to World Cup glory?

- A: Franz Beckenbauer
- B: Lothar Mattäus
- C: Paul Breitner
- D: Fritz Walter

24

When did Ghana make their debut at the World Cup finals?

- A: 1998
- B: 2002
- C: 2006
- D: 2010

If you would like to use your 50:50 please turn to page 307
If you would like to use your Ask The Audience please turn to page 325
Turn to the answer section on page 336 to find out if you've won £32,000!

10 ◆ £32,000 WORLD CUP

25

After South Africa, which was the first team to qualify for the 2010 World Cup finals?

- A: The Netherlands
- B: England
- C: Japan
- D: Brazil

26

Which of these groups at the 2010 World Cup finals did not include an African team?

- A: C
- B: D
- C: E
- D: F

27

Which of these teams did not drop a point in qualifying for 2010?

- A: Italy
- B: Germany
- C: Spain
- D: Slovakia

28

At which World Cup did the legendary Pelé make his final appearance on the world stage?

- A: 1978
- B: 1974
- C: 1970
- D: 1966

If you would like to use your 50:50 please turn to page 307
If you would like to use your Ask The Audience please turn to page 325
Turn to the answer section on page 336 to find out if you've won £32,000!

10 ◆ £32,000 WORLD CUP

29

Including 2010, which is the most southerly city to have hosted the World Cup final?

- A: Mexico City
- B: Santiago
- C: Johannesburg
- D: Montevideo

30

Which was the first World Cup tournament to use a black and white match ball?

- A: 1970
- B: 1974
- C: 1978
- D: 1982

31

After World War II, which was the first communist country to reach the World Cup final?

- A: Czechoslovakia
- B: Soviet Union
- C: Hungary
- D: Yugoslavia

If you would like to use your 50:50 please turn to page 307
If you would like to use your Ask The Audience please turn to page 325
Turn to the answer section on page 336 to find out if you've won £32,000!

10 ◆ £32,000 EUROPEAN

1

Which of these was the brainchild of a Dutch reporter named Anton Witkamp?

- A: UEFA Cup
- B: UEFA Super Cup
- C: Golden goal
- D: Penalty shoot-outs

2

In 1972, which trophy was designed and crafted by the Bertoni workshops in Milan?

- A: UEFA Cup
- B: European Cup
- C: UEFA Super Cup
- D: Cup Winners' Cup

3

In 1992, which was the last club to win the European Cup before it became the Champions League?

- A: AC Milan
- B: Real Madrid
- C: PSV Eindhoven
- D: Barcelona

4

How many times has the host nation won the European Championship?

- A: Never
- B: Once
- C: Twice
- D: Three

If you would like to use your 50:50 please turn to page 307
If you would like to use your Ask The Audience please turn to page 325
Turn to the answer section on page 336 to find out if you've won £32,000!

10 ◆ £32,000 EUROPEAN

5

Who are the only Turkish club to have won the UEFA Cup?

- A: Fenerbahçe
- B: Trabzonspor
- C: Galatasaray
- D: Besiktas

6

RCD Espanyol would play a local derby against which other Spanish team?

- A: Real Madrid
- B: Valencia
- C: Barcelona
- D: Athletic Bilbao

7

By what nickname is Carlo Ancelotti affectionately known in his homeland?

- A: Carlita
- B: Carlotta
- C: Carletto
- D: Carletta

8

Who once worked as an interpreter for Bobby Robson during his time managing a European club?

- A: Marco van Basten
- B: Gerd Müller
- C: José Mourinho
- D: David Ginola

If you would like to use your 50:50 please turn to page 307
If you would like to use your Ask The Audience please turn to page 325
Turn to the answer section on page 336 to find out if you've won £32,000!

10 ◆ £32,000 EUROPEAN

9

What is the distinctive predominant colour of Fiorentina's first-choice strip?

- A: Gold
- B: Pink
- C: Brown
- D: Purple

10

Which is the first Israeli club to qualify for the group stage of the Champions League?

- A: Hapoel Haifa
- B: Maccabi Netanya
- C: Maccabi Haifa
- D: Hapoel Tel-Aviv

11

Which of these is one of only two managers to have won all three main UEFA club competitions?

- A: Arsène Wenger
- B: Udo Lattek
- C: Carlo Ancelotti
- D: Ernst Happel

12

Which ground holds the record for the highest gate at a European Cup or Champions League final?

- A: Stade de France
- B: Hampden Park
- C: Bernabéu Stadium
- D: San Siro

If you would like to use your 50:50 please turn to page 307
If you would like to use your Ask The Audience please turn to page 325
Turn to the answer section on page 336 to find out if you've won £32,000!

10 ◆ £32,000 EUROPEAN

13

Which of these is a Belgian football club?

- A: Germinal Beerschot
- B: VVV Venlo
- C: AaB
- D: Tampere United

14

How many teams were there in the 2009/10 season of the German Bundesliga?

- A: Sixteen
- B: Eighteen
- C: Twenty
- D: Twenty-two

15

Which country had the greatest number of players on the men's shortlist for the 2009 FIFA World Player?

- A: Italy
- B: Portugal
- C: Spain
- D: Brazil

If you would like to use your 50:50 please turn to page 307
If you would like to use your Ask The Audience please turn to page 325
Turn to the answer section on page 336 to find out if you've won £32,000!

10 ◆ £32,000 DOMESTIC

1

If the 2009/10 Premier League ends alphabetically, how many Lancashire teams are in the top six?

- A: None
- B: One
- C: Two
- D: Three

2

What colour is the star on the badge of Aston Villa?

- A: Red
- B: White
- C: Gold
- D: Blue

3

Where do St Johnstone play their home matches?

- A: Dundee
- B: Perth
- C: Stirling
- D: Edinburgh

4

In 2006, whom did Mick McCarthy succeed as manager of Wolverhampton Wanderers?

- A: Bruce Rioch
- B: Mark McGhee
- C: Dave Jones
- D: Glenn Hoddle

If you would like to use your 50:50 please turn to page 307
If you would like to use your Ask The Audience please turn to page 325
Turn to the answer section on page 336 to find out if you've won £32,000!

10 ♦ £32,000 DOMESTIC

5

In 2009, which bank signed a four-year deal to become Liverpool's main sponsors?

- A: HSBC
- B: Standard Chartered
- C: Lloyds TSB
- D: Credit Suisse

6

Which of these is not one of the original twelve members of the Football League?

- A: Everton
- B: Burnley
- C: Stoke City
- D: Manchester City

7

After whom is the former North Bank at West Ham United's home ground now named?

- A: Bobby Moore
- B: Geoff Hurst
- C: Trevor Brooking
- D: Ron Greenwood

8

Which club won the FA Cup in the 1970s while in the second division?

- A: Ipswich Town
- B: West Ham United
- C: Chelsea
- D: Southampton

If you would like to use your 50:50 please turn to page 307
If you would like to use your Ask The Audience please turn to page 325
Turn to the answer section on page 336 to find out if you've won £32,000!

10 ◆ £32,000 DOMESTIC

9

Which is the only club Peter Shilton has managed?

- A: Peterborough United
- B: Portsmouth
- C: Port Vale
- D: Plymouth Argyle

10

Between 2004 and 2007, which club won the Scottish third, second and first division titles?

- A: Partick Thistle
- B: Gretna
- C: St Johnstone
- D: Livingston

11

Who, besides Blackpool, were known as the 'Seasiders'?

- A: Scarborough
- B: Grimsby Town
- C: Plymouth Argyle
- D: Scunthorpe United

12

What follows Wick to give the name of a Scottish Highland League club?

- A: School
- B: Pupils
- C: University
- D: Academy

If you would like to use your 50:50 please turn to page 307
If you would like to use your Ask The Audience please turn to page 325
Turn to the answer section on page 336 to find out if you've won £32,000!

10 ◆ £32,000 DOMESTIC

13

According to an old saying, it's lucky for Spurs when the year ends in what number?

- A: 1
- B: 3
- C: 5
- D: 8

14

What nationality is the Chelsea goalkeeper Ross Turnbull?

- A: Canadian
- B: South African
- C: English
- D: Australian

15

Which was the first professional British league club to wear sponsored shirts?

- A: Manchester United
- B: Arsenal
- C: Liverpool
- D: Rangers

If you would like to use your 50:50 please turn to page 307
If you would like to use your Ask The Audience please turn to page 325
Turn to the answer section on page 336 to find out if you've won £32,000!

50:50

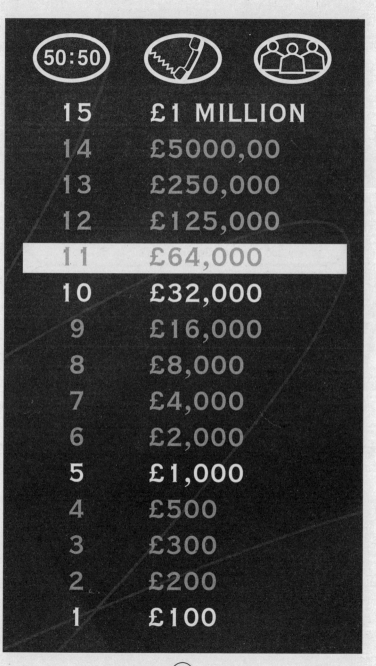

15	£1 MILLION
14	£5000,00
13	£250,000
12	£125,000
11	£64,000
10	£32,000
9	£16,000
8	£8,000
7	£4,000
6	£2,000
5	£1,000
4	£500
3	£300
2	£200
1	£100

11 ◆ £64,000 WORLD CUP

1

Which was the last World Cup finals for which France failed to qualify?

- A: 1982
- B: 1986
- C: 1990
- D: 1994

2

The opening match of the 2006 World Cup finals took place in which German city?

- A: Berlin
- B: Munich
- C: Dortmund
- D: Frankfurt

3

At the 1990 World Cup finals, which team topped their group with a negative goal difference?

- A: Spain
- B: Italy
- C: Brazil
- D: Cameroon

4

Who were the first champions not to qualify automatically for the next World Cup finals?

- A: Italy
- B: France
- C: Argentina
- D: Brazil

If you would like to use your 50:50 please turn to page 308
If you would like to use your Ask The Audience please turn to page 325
Turn to the answer section on page 336 to find out if you've won £64,000!

11 ◆ £64,000 WORLD CUP

5

Who provided the biggest upset at the 1994 World Cup by beating Germany *en route* to the semis?

- A: Romania
- B: Nigeria
- C: Bulgaria
- D: Saudi Arabia

6

The Brazilian World Cup-winner Rai is the brother of which other Brazilian legend?

- A: Pelé
- B: Jairzinho
- C: Socrates
- D: Romário

7

Which World Cup tournament was the first to include thirty-two teams?

- A: 1990
- B: 1994
- C: 1998
- D: 2002

8

In 2006, who was knocked out of the World Cup finals without conceding a goal?

- A: Switzerland
- B: Ecuador
- C: Ukraine
- D: Portugal

If you would like to use your 50:50 please turn to page 308
If you would like to use your Ask The Audience please turn to page 325
Turn to the answer section on page 336 to find out if you've won £64,000!

11 ◆ £64,000 WORLD CUP

9

Ottmar Hitzfeld was head coach of which team during their 2010 World Cup campaign?

- A: Serbia
- B: Slovakia
- C: Switzerland
- D: Spain

10

Who was presented with the Golden Ball Award at the 1994 World Cup finals?

- A: Dunga
- B: Roberto Baggio
- C: Tomas Brolin
- D: Romário

11

In 2002, who became the first player to appear in the final of three consecutive World Cups?

- A: Roberto Carlos
- B: Emerson
- C: Cafu
- D: Gilberto

12

Who managed Germany to third place at the 2006 World Cup finals?

- A: Jürgen Klinsmann
- B: Rudi Völler
- C: Joachim Löw
- D: Erich Ribbeck

If you would like to use your 50:50 please turn to page 308
If you would like to use your Ask The Audience please turn to page 325
Turn to the answer section on page 336 to find out if you've won £64,000!

11 ◆ £64,000 WORLD CUP

13

Shane Smeltz was which country's top scorer in the qualifying games for South Africa 2010?

- A: Australia
- B: USA
- C: Switzerland
- D: New Zealand

14

Milovan Rajevac coached which African team to the 2010 World Cup finals?

- A: Ghana
- B: Côte d'Ivoire
- C: Nigeria
- D: South Africa

15

Who did Costa Rica play off against for a place in the 2010 World Cup finals?

- A: Bolivia
- B: Uruguay
- C: Ecuador
- D: Colombia

16

In which World Cup final was a penalty awarded after only two minutes of normal time?

- A: 1986
- B: 1982
- C: 1978
- D: 1974

If you would like to use your 50:50 please turn to page 308
If you would like to use your Ask The Audience please turn to page 326
Turn to the answer section on page 336 to find out if you've won £64,000!

11 ◆ £64,000 WORLD CUP

17

Who did Germany defeat 4-2 in the opening game of the 2006 World Cup finals?

- A: Ecuador
- B: Paraguay
- C: Costa Rica
- D: Mexico

18

Which member of Scotland's 1998 World Cup squad was 40 years old just twelve days after the final?

- A: Tom Boyd
- B: Gordon Durie
- C: Jim Leighton
- D: Tosh McKinlay

19

Grzegorz Lato, the top scorer at the 1974 World Cup finals, played for which country?

- A: Soviet Union
- B: Hungary
- C: Poland
- D: Czechoslovakia

20

Who won their first-ever World Cup qualifier when they beat Austria 1-0 in 1990?

- A: San Marino
- B: Liechtenstein
- C: Faroe Islands
- D: Andorra

If you would like to use your 50:50 please turn to page 308
If you would like to use your Ask The Audience please turn to page 326
Turn to the answer section on page 336 to find out if you've won £64,000!

11 ◆ £64,000 WORLD CUP

21

Which country won the World Cup but refused to play in the tournament four years later?

- A: Argentina
- B: Italy
- C: Uruguay
- D: Brazil

22

Which country held and was responsible for the Jules Rimet trophy during World War II?

- A: France
- B: Brazil
- C: Uruguay
- D: Italy

23

In which year did Slovenia make their debut at the World Cup finals?

- A: 1994
- B: 1998
- C: 2002
- D: 2006

24

Brazil's defeat by Uruguay at the 1950 World Cup inspired what new Spanish noun?

- A: Desperanzo
- B: Maracanazo
- C: Uruguanzo
- D: Copanzo

If you would like to use your 50:50 please turn to page 308
If you would like to use your Ask The Audience please turn to page 326
Turn to the answer section on page 336 to find out if you've won £64,000!

11 ◆ £64,000 EUROPEAN

1

Which European trophy is the heaviest?

- A: Champions League
- B: European Championship
- C: UEFA Super Cup
- D: Europa League

2

In 1992, who lost the last European Cup final before it became the Champions League?

- A: Lazio
- B: Sampdoria
- C: Juventus
- D: Inter Milan

3

As of 2008, which was the last country to win the European Championship as the host nation?

- A: France
- B: Spain
- C: Italy
- D: Germany

4

Approximately, what was the gate at the first European Cup final in 1955?

- A: 18,000
- B: 38,000
- C: 78,000
- D: 98,000

If you would like to use your 50:50 please turn to page 308
If you would like to use your Ask The Audience please turn to page 326
Turn to the answer section on page 336 to find out if you've won £64,000!

11 ◆ £64,000 EUROPEAN

5

Which country has the most teams to have played in the Champions League, twelve in total?

- A: Italy
- B: Germany
- C: England
- D: Spain

6

Raymond Goethals was the first Belgian to coach a Champions League-winning team – which one?

- A: Borussia Dortmund
- B: Steaua Bucharest
- C: Marseille
- D: PSV Eindhoven

7

When the European Cup started in 1955, how many teams competed in the first round?

- A: Four
- B: Eight
- C: Sixteen
- D: Thirty-two

8

Which was the first Iron Curtain team to reach the European Cup final?

- A: Red Star Moscow
- B: Dynamo Kiev
- C: Steaua Bucharest
- D: Partizan Belgrade

If you would like to use your 50:50 please turn to page 308
If you would like to use your Ask The Audience please turn to page 326
Turn to the answer section on page 336 to find out if you've won £64,000!

11 ◆ £64,000 EUROPEAN

9

Sampdoria ground share the Stadio Luigi Ferraris with which other club?

- A: Siena
- B: Catania
- C: Genoa
- D: Bologna

10

Which club held the Bundesliga championship going into the 2009/10 season?

- A: Bayern Munich
- B: VfL Wolfsburg
- C: FC Schalke 04
- D: Borussia Dortmund

11

Which was the first club to win UEFA's original three major competitions?

- A: Bayern Munich
- B: Ajax
- C: AC Milan
- D: Juventus

12

In which city is the Spanish club Osasuna based?

- A: Seville
- B: Granada
- C: Malaga
- D: Pamplona

If you would like to use your 50:50 please turn to page 308
If you would like to use your Ask The Audience please turn to page 326
Turn to the answer section on page 336 to find out if you've won £64,000!

11 ◆ £64,000 EUROPEAN

13

Joan Laporta became the president of which club in 2003?

- A: Barcelona
- B: Porto
- C: Benfica
- D: Real Madrid

If you would like to use your 50:50 please turn to page 308
If you would like to use your Ask The Audience please turn to page 326
Turn to the answer section on page 336 to find out if you've won £64,000!

11 ◆ £64,000 DOMESTIC

1

Which England player has the middle names McLeod Cooper?

- A: Wes Brown
- B: Glen Johnson
- C: Joleon Lescott
- D: James Milner

2

The US businessman Stan Kroenke is a major shareholder of which club?

- A: Arsenal
- B: Everton
- C: Manchester United
- D: Tottenham Hotspur

3

If the 2009/10 Premier League ended alphabetically, how many London teams would be relegated?

- A: None
- B: One
- C: Two
- D: Three

4

On which road does Wolverhampton Wanderers' Molineux Stadium stand?

- A: Alma Road
- B: Waterloo Road
- C: Inkermann Road
- D: Blenheim Road

If you would like to use your 50:50 please turn to page 308
If you would like to use your Ask The Audience please turn to page 326
Turn to the answer section on page 336 to find out if you've won £64,000!

11 ◆ £64,000 DOMESTIC

5

Which team originally played in blue and white halved shirts with blue shorts?

- A: Liverpool
- B: Manchester United
- C: Nottingham Forest
- D: Newcastle United

6

In the 2009/10 season, which of these Welsh internationals actually played for a Welsh club?

- A: Joe Ledley
- B: Owain Tudur Jones
- C: Jack Collison
- D: Lewin Nyatanga

7

Which Welsh legend died in February 2004 aged 72?

- A: Ivor Allchurch
- B: John Charles
- C: Cliff Jones
- D: Trevor Ford

8

'Keep Right On Till The End Of The Road' is the anthem of which club?

- A: Manchester City
- B: Birmingham City
- C: Leicester City
- D: Coventry City

If you would like to use your 50:50 please turn to page 308
If you would like to use your Ask The Audience please turn to page 326
Turn to the answer section on page 336 to find out if you've won £64,000!

11 ◆ £64,000 DOMESTIC

9

Which Rangers player has been dubbed the Scottish Wayne Rooney?

- A: Steven Lennon
- B: Andrew Shinnie
- C: John Fleck
- D: Jamie Ness

10

In which year were the last Home International Championships held?

- A: 1982
- B: 1986
- C: 1980
- D: 1984

11

Which football club's motto is *Arte et labore*?

- A: Blackburn Rovers
- B: Aston Villa
- C: Everton
- D: Fulham

12

What is the title of Tony Adams's autobiography?

- A: *Addicted*
- B: *Driven*
- C: *Hooked*
- D: *Committed*

If you would like to use your 50:50 please turn to page 308
If you would like to use your Ask The Audience please turn to page 326
Turn to the answer section on page 336 to find out if you've won £64,000!

13

Which of these Scottish league clubs is based in Glasgow?

- A: Partick Thistle
- B: Livingston
- C: St Johnstone
- D: Albion Rovers

If you would like to use your 50:50 please turn to page 308
If you would like to use your Ask The Audience please turn to page 326
Turn to the answer section on page 336 to find out if you've won £64,000!

50:50

15	£1 MILLION
14	£5000,00
13	£250,000
12	£125,000
11	£64,000
10	£32,000
9	£16,000
8	£8,000
7	£4,000
6	£2,000
5	£1,000
4	£500
3	£300
2	£200
1	£100

12 ◆ £125,000 WORLD CUP

1

Who was the only Brazilian in the Mastercard All-Star Team from the 2006 World Cup finals?

- A: Ronaldo
- B: Roberto
- C: Ronaldinho
- D: Robinho

2

What nationality was the sculptor who designed the Jules Rimet Trophy?

- A: French
- B: Finnish
- C: Swiss
- D: Italian

3

Which future England manager was part of the 1950 England World Cup finals squad?

- A: Alf Ramsey
- B: Don Revie
- C: Joe Mercer
- D: Ron Greenwood

4

What did Savo Milosevic, Philip Cocu and Lee Woon-Jae all do at the 2006 World Cup finals?

- A: Fail a drugs test
- B: Get four yellow cards
- C: Score hat-tricks
- D: Get their 100th cap

If you would like to use your 50:50 please turn to page 309
If you would like to use your Ask The Audience please turn to page 326
Turn to the answer section on page 337 to find out if you've won £125,000!

12 ◆ £125,000 WORLD CUP

5

In 1954, which team scored twenty-five goals in four matches on their way to the final?

- A: West Germany
- B: Hungary
- C: Austria
- D: Uruguay

6

Prior to 2010, how often has the World Cup final featured teams from the same continent?

- A: Eight
- B: Nine
- C: Ten
- D: Eleven

7

Oscar Tabárez coached which nation to the 2010 World Cup finals?

- A: Uruguay
- B: Paraguay
- C: Argentina
- D: Chile

8

Which team were eliminated at the group stage in 1974 despite being unbeaten?

- A: Poland
- B: Scotland
- C: East Germany
- D: Argentina

If you would like to use your 50:50 please turn to page 309
If you would like to use your Ask The Audience please turn to page 326
Turn to the answer section on page 337 to find out if you've won £125,000!

12 ◆ £125,000 WORLD CUP

9

Which was the first World Cup final in which one of the teams did not score a goal?

- A: 1982
- B: 1986
- C: 1990
- D: 1994

10

Which European team won the final of the 2009 Under-17 World Cup?

- A: Slovenia
- B: Slovakia
- C: Serbia
- D: Switzerland

11

Who lifted the trophy as captain of Brazil at the 1994 World Cup finals?

- A: Bebeto
- B: Dunga
- C: Jorginho
- D: Rai

12

Which World Cup final was the first ever to be decided by a penalty shoot-out?

- A: 1934
- B: 1978
- C: 1994
- D: 2006

If you would like to use your 50:50 please turn to page 309
If you would like to use your Ask The Audience please turn to page 326
Turn to the answer section on page 337 to find out if you've won £125,000!

12 ◆ £125,000 WORLD CUP

13

FIFA regulations state a World Cup finals squad must include how many goalkeepers?

- A: One
- B: Two
- C: Three
- D: Four

14

What nickname has been given to the 2010 venue Mbombela Stadium?

- A: Elephant Stadium
- B: Giraffe Stadium
- C: Rhino Stadium
- D: Zebra Stadium

15

Aaron Mokoena is the most-capped player of which 2010 qualifier?

- A: Nigeria
- B: South Africa
- C: Ghana
- D: Côte d'Ivoire

16

Prior to 2010, which is the only other World Cup for which Greece qualified?

- A: 2006
- B: 2002
- C: 1998
- D: 1994

If you would like to use your 50:50 please turn to page 309
If you would like to use your Ask The Audience please turn to page 326
Turn to the answer section on page 337 to find out if you've won £125,000!

12 ◆ £125,000 WORLD CUP

17

Bob Bradley was head coach of which team during their 2010 World Cup campaign?

- A: New Zealand
- B: USA
- C: Australia
- D: Jamaica

18

Which of these countries did not come bottom of their 2010 qualifying group?

- A: Malta
- B: Moldova
- C: Iceland
- D: FYR Macedonia

If you would like to use your 50:50 please turn to page 309
If you would like to use your Ask The Audience please turn to page 326
Turn to the answer section on page 337 to find out if you've won £125,000!

12 ◆ £125,000 EUROPEAN

1

What kind of animal was Benelucky, the mascot of Euro 2000?

- A: Lion
- B: Rabbit
- C: Bear
- D: Fox

2

Who was reinstated into Euro 92 when Yugoslavia was disqualified?

- A: Sweden
- B: Belgium
- C: Finland
- D: Denmark

3

As of April 2010, which international manager has won all three major UEFA club titles?

- A: Fabio Capello
- B: Raymond Domenech
- C: Marcello Lippi
- D: Giovanni Trapattoni

4

Who was the leading goalscorer in the UEFA Cup?

- A: Alan Shearer
- B: Henrik Larsson
- C: Jupp Heynckes
- D: Dieter Müller

If you would like to use your 50:50 please turn to page 309
If you would like to use your Ask The Audience please turn to page 326
Turn to the answer section on page 337 to find out if you've won £125,000!

12 ◆ £125,000 EUROPEAN

5

How much money does a club receive from UEFA for winning the Champions League final?

- A: €3 million
- B: €5 million
- C: €7 million
- D: €9 million

6

What was inaugurated at the suggestion of the French sports journalist Gabriel Hanot?

- A: UEFA Cup
- B: European Cup
- C: Intertoto Cup
- D: Cup Winners' Cup

7

In which year was the last Cup Winners' Cup final played?

- A: 1996
- B: 1997
- C: 1998
- D: 1999

8

Which team won the Cup Winners' Cup most often, with four titles?

- A: AC Milan
- B: Real Madrid
- C: Barcelona
- D: Ajax

If you would like to use your 50:50 please turn to page 309
If you would like to use your Ask The Audience please turn to page 326–327
Turn to the answer section on page 337 to find out if you've won £125,000!

12 ◆ £125,000 EUROPEAN

9

Which Italian club is sometimes referred to as the 'Rossoneri'?

- A: AC Milan
- B: Lazio
- C: Sampdoria
- D: Roma

10

Which of these is a Brazilian player on the books with FC Porto for the 2009/10 season?

- A: Thor
- B: Wolverine
- C: Hulk
- D: Batman

If you would like to use your 50:50 please turn to page 309
If you would like to use your Ask The Audience please turn to page 327
Turn to the answer section on page 337 to find out if you've won £125,000!

12 ◆ £125,000 DOMESTIC

1

The Metro FM Stand forms the south end of which ground?

- A: St James' Park
- B: Stadium of Light
- C: Riverside Stadium
- D: Victoria Park

2

Which club was formed in 1880 as West Gorton St Marks, becoming Ardwick FC in 1887?

- A: Manchester City
- B: Arsenal
- C: Tottenham Hotspur
- D: Preston North End

3

For which club did Bill Shankly, Tommy Docherty and Howard Kendall all play?

- A: Tranmere Rovers
- B: Crewe Alexandra
- C: Bury
- D: Preston North End

4

In which year did the English FA first join FIFA?

- A: 1905
- B: 1910
- C: 1920
- D: 1925

If you would like to use your 50:50 please turn to page 309
If you would like to use your Ask The Audience please turn to page 327
Turn to the answer section on page 337 to find out if you've won £125,000!

12 ◆ £125,000 DOMESTIC

5

At the start of the 2009/10 season, which of these teams had an English manager?

- A: Aberdeen
- B: Falkirk
- C: Celtic
- D: Dundee

6

At Gillingham's Priestfield Stadium, there is a stand named after which famous commentator?

- A: John Motson
- B: Brian Moore
- C: Barry Davies
- D: David Coleman

7

In 2002, which club did David Moyes leave to take up the manager's job at Everton?

- A: Blackpool
- B: Bury
- C: Preston North End
- D: Tranmere Rovers

8

Frogmore the Frog is a mascot of which club?

- A: Portsmouth
- B: Aston Villa
- C: Middlesbrough
- D: Sunderland

If you would like to use your 50:50 please turn to page 309
If you would like to use your Ask The Audience please turn to page 327
Turn to the answer section on page 337 to find out if you've won £125,000!

12 ◆ £125,000 DOMESTIC

9

Since 2006, what does the 'S' stand for in the name of the Welsh premier league club TNS?

- A: Saints
- B: Sabres
- C: Solutions
- D: Shropshire

10

Who scored the goal that won the 2009 Scottish FA Cup final for Rangers?

- A: Kris Boyd
- B: Nacho Novo
- C: Kenny Miller
- D: Madjid Bougherra

If you would like to use your 50:50 please turn to page 309
If you would like to use your Ask The Audience please turn to page 327
Turn to the answer section on page 337 to find out if you've won £125,000!

50:50

15	£1 MILLION
14	£5000,00
13	£250,000
12	£125,000
11	£64,000
10	£32,000
9	£16,000
8	£8,000
7	£4,000
6	£2,000
5	£1,000
4	£500
3	£300
2	£200
1	£100

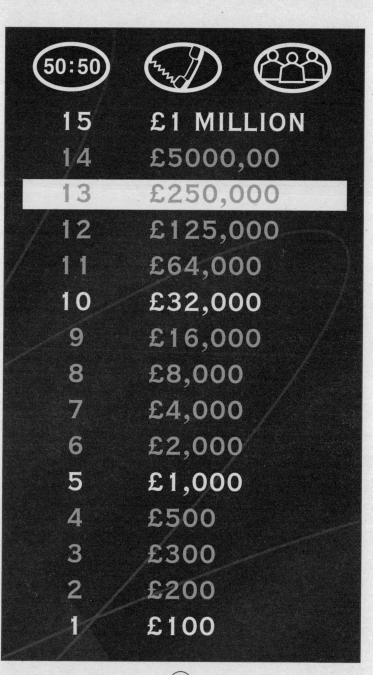

13 ◆ £250,000 WORLD CUP

1

Which of these countries qualified for the 1994 tournament?

- A: Denmark
- B: England
- C: Switzerland
- D: France

2

Which World Cup final was contested by teams that had each won the trophy three times?

- A: 1982
- B: 1990
- C: 1994
- D: 2006

3

The 2010 official mascot is Zakumi, from 'ZA' for South Africa and 'kumi' meaning what?

- A: Leopard
- B: Pride
- C: Ten
- D: Champion

4

As announced in 2009, how many Brazilian cities will host matches at the 2014 World Cup finals?

- A: Eight
- B: Ten
- C: Twelve
- D: Fourteen

If you would like to use your 50:50 please turn to page 310
If you would like to use your Ask The Audience please turn to page 327
Turn to the answer section on page 337 to find out if you've won £250,000!

13 ◆ £250,000 WORLD CUP

5

In the 1966 World Cup finals, at which ground did North Korea defeat Italy 1-0?

- A: Roker Park
- B: Goodison Park
- C: Ayresome Park
- D: Villa Park

6

Which team withdrew from the 1950 World Cup as FIFA would not allow them to play in bare feet?

- A: Bolivia
- B: India
- C: Palestine
- D: Egypt

7

Which country hosted the inaugural Women's World Cup in 1991?

- A: Sweden
- B: Germany
- C: USA
- D: China

8

In 1930, how many European teams competed in the first World Cup finals?

- A: Four
- B: Five
- C: Six
- D: Seven

If you would like to use your 50:50 please turn to page 310
If you would like to use your Ask The Audience please turn to page 327
Turn to the answer section on page 337 to find out if you've won £250,000!

13 ◆ £250,000 WORLD CUP

9

By what score did Brazil win both their semi-final and final at the 1958 World Cup?

- A: 1-0
- B: 3-1
- C: 4-0
- D: 5-2

10

Which was the first African nation ever to compete in the World Cup finals?

- A: Algeria
- B: Egypt
- C: Ghana
- D: Nigeria

If you would like to use your 50:50 please turn to page 310
If you would like to use your Ask The Audience please turn to page 327
Turn to the answer section on page 337 to find out if you've won £250,000!

13 ◆ £250,000 EUROPEAN

1

Who were the only French winners of the Cup Winners' Cup?

- A: Lyon
- B: Lille
- C: Auxerre
- D: Paris Saint-Germain

2

Not counting replays, how many Cup Winners' Cup finals were played over two legs?

- A: None
- B: One
- C: Two
- D: Three

3

In which year was the last two-legged final of the UEFA Cup played?

- A: 1994
- B: 1995
- C: 1996
- D: 1997

4

For which club was Sven-Göran Eriksson the coach between 1982 and 1984, and 1988 and 1992?

- A: Gothenburg
- B: Benfica
- C: Sampdoria
- D: Paris Saint-Germain

If you would like to use your 50:50 please turn to page 310
If you would like to use your Ask The Audience please turn to page 327
Turn to the answer section on page 337 to find out if you've won £250,000!

13 ◆ £250,000 EUROPEAN

5

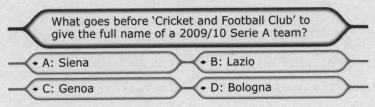

What goes before 'Cricket and Football Club' to give the full name of a 2009/10 Serie A team?

- A: Siena
- B: Lazio
- C: Genoa
- D: Bologna

If you would like to use your 50:50 please turn to page 310
If you would like to use your Ask The Audience please turn to page 327
Turn to the answer section on page 337 to find out if you've won £250,000!

13 ◆ £250,000 DOMESTIC

1

To the 2009/10 season, which of these clubs has had four separate stints in the Premier League?

- A: Fulham
- B: Sunderland
- C: Middlesbrough
- D: Birmingham City

2

Which non-West Ham United player features in the Champions Statue outside Upton Park?

- A: George Cohen
- B: Bobby Charlton
- C: Ray Wilson
- D: Alan Ball

3

The roof of which Scottish stadium is adorned with 'KEEP CIGARETTES AWAY FROM THE MATCH'?

- A: Fir Park
- B: Tannadice Park
- C: New Douglas Park
- D: New St Mirren Park

4

Which of these Northern Irish league clubs is not based in Belfast?

- A: Institute
- B: Linfield
- C: Cliftonville
- D: Glentoran

If you would like to use your 50:50 please turn to page 310
If you would like to use your Ask The Audience please turn to page 327
Turn to the answer section on page 337 to find out if you've won £250,000!

13 ◆ £250,000 DOMESTIC

5

Who holds the record for the most appearances for Manchester City?

- A: Alan Oakes
- B: Mike Summerbee
- C: Joe Corrigan
- D: Colin Bell

If you would like to use your 50:50 please turn to page 310
If you would like to use your Ask The Audience please turn to page 327
Turn to the answer section on page 337 to find out if you've won £250,000!

50:50

15	£1 MILLION
14	£5000,00
13	£250,000
12	£125,000
11	£64,000
10	£32,000
9	£16,000
8	£8,000
7	£4,000
6	£2,000
5	£1,000
4	£500
3	£300
2	£200
1	£100

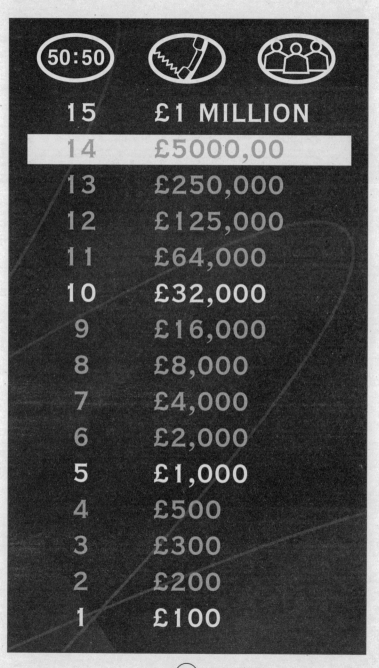

14 ◆ £500,000 WORLD CUP

1

Which team won the Most Entertaining Team award at the 2006 World Cup tournament?

- A: Croatia
- B: Brazil
- C: Spain
- D: Portugal

2

Which was the only team not to score a goal at the 2006 World Cup finals?

- A: Iran
- B: Angola
- C: Trinidad & Tobago
- D: Togo

3

Which computer company offered laptop buyers a 66 per cent rebate if England won the 2006 World Cup?

- A: Apple
- B: Dell
- C: Samsung
- D: Toshiba

4

At the 1994 World Cup, who did Bulgaria beat after a run of seventeen winless World Cup matches?

- A: Greece
- B: Nigeria
- C: Bolivia
- D: South Korea

If you would like to use your 50:50 please turn to page 311
If you would like to use your Ask The Audience please turn to page 327
Turn to the answer section on page 337 to find out if you've won £500,000!

14 ◆ £500,000 WORLD CUP

5

'A Time To Make Friends' was the official motto of which World Cup tournament?

- A: 1998, France
- B: 1994, USA
- C: 2006, Germany
- D: 2002, Korea/Japan

6

At which World Cup was the award for the Best Young Player made for the first time?

- A: 1994
- B: 1998
- C: 2002
- D: 2006

7

Which team shared the 1998 Fair Play award with England?

- A: The Netherlands
- B: Spain
- C: France
- D: Brazil

8

At which stage were England eliminated from the 1958 World Cup finals?

- A: Qualifying
- B: Group stage
- C: Quarter-final
- D: Semi-final

If you would like to use your 50:50 please turn to page 311
If you would like to use your Ask The Audience please turn to page 327
Turn to the answer section on page 337 to find out if you've won £500,000!

14 ◆ £500,000 WORLD CUP

9

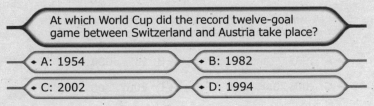

At which World Cup did the record twelve-goal game between Switzerland and Austria take place?

- A: 1954
- B: 1982
- C: 2002
- D: 1994

If you would like to use your 50:50 please turn to page 311
If you would like to use your Ask The Audience please turn to page 327
Turn to the answer section on page 337 to find out if you've won £500,000!

14 ◆ £500,000 EUROPEAN

1

A cartoon version of a boy named Kinas was the mascot of which European Championship?

- A: Euro 1996
- B: Euro 2000
- C: Euro 2004
- D: Euro 2008

2

The Italian club Torino are nicknamed after which animal?

- A: Bull
- B: Stag
- C: Eagle
- D: Lion

3

Which country hosted the final of the first European Nations Cup in 1960?

- A: West Germany
- B: Czechoslovakia
- C: France
- D: Hungary

4

In October 2009, Abel Resino was sacked as the coach of which Spanish club?

- A: Atlético Madrid
- B: Deportivo La Coruña
- C: Sevilla
- D: Espanyol

If you would like to use your 50:50 please turn to page 311
If you would like to use your Ask The Audience please turn to page 327
Turn to the answer section on page 337 to find out if you've won £500,000!

14 ◆ £500,000 DOMESTIC

1

How old was Andy Millen when he played for St Mirren against Hearts in March 2008?

- A: 15
- B: 16
- C: 39
- D: 42

2

What is Mark Hughes's first forename?

- A: Lawrence
- B: Lionel
- C: Lancaster
- D: Leslie

3

Which was the first British ground to use floodlights?

- A: Bramall Lane
- B: St Andrew's
- C: Ninian Park
- D: Pittodrie Stadium

4

In 1881, where did England play their first home international outside of London?

- A: Birmingham
- B: Bolton
- C: Bristol
- D: Blackburn

If you would like to use your 50:50 please turn to page 311
If you would like to use your Ask The Audience please turn to page 327
Turn to the answer section on page 337 to find out if you've won £500,000!

50:50

15	£1 MILLION
14	£5000,00
13	£250,000
12	£125,000
11	£64,000
10	£32,000
9	£16,000
8	£8,000
7	£4,000
6	£2,000
5	£1,000
4	£500
3	£300
2	£200
1	£100

15 ◆ £1,000,000 WORLD CUP

1

In 1986, who set a record for being sent off after only 56 seconds of a World Cup finals game?

- A: Sergio Santin
- B: Miguel Bossio
- C: Alfonso Pereira
- D: José Batista

2

José Altafini played for Brazil in the 1958 World Cup and for which other country in 1962?

- A: Uruguay
- B: Portugal
- C: Argentina
- D: Italy

3

In the November 2009 FIFA rankings, which was the lowest-ranked team at the 2010 tournament?

- A: New Zealand
- B: South Africa
- C: North Korea
- D: Honduras

4

Prior to 2010, what is the furthest Mexico have progressed in the World Cup finals?

- A: Quarter-finals
- B: Semi-finals
- C: Final
- D: Group stage

If you would like to use your 50:50 please turn to page 312
If you would like to use your Ask The Audience please turn to page 327–328
Turn to the answer section on page 338 to find out if you've won £1,000,000!

15 ◆ £1,000,000 WORLD CUP

5

In 1954, who did Austria beat 7-5 in the World Cup match with the highest ever number of goals?

- A: Peru
- B: Switzerland
- C: Bolivia
- D: Portugal

6

Which was the first African country to win a match at a World Cup finals tournament?

- A: South Africa
- B: Egypt
- C: Cameroon
- D: Tunisia

7

Which city hosted the third/fourth play-off place at the 2006 World Cup finals?

- A: Dortmund
- B: Munich
- C: Stuttgart
- D: Frankfurt

If you would like to use your 50:50 please turn to page 312
If you would like to use your Ask The Audience please turn to page 328
Turn to the answer section on page 338 to find out if you've won £1,000,000!

15 ◆ £1,000,000 EUROPEAN

1

How many member associations are affiliated to UEFA?

- A: Forty-six
- B: Fifty-three
- C: Sixty-one
- D: Seventy

2

Which was the last country to win a third/fourth play-off match in the European Championship?

- A: Yugoslavia
- B: Hungary
- C: Czechoslovakia
- D: Poland

3

In which European city would a derby take place between clubs called Levadia and Flora?

- A: Minsk
- B: Tallinn
- C: Zagreb
- D: Bratislava

If you would like to use your 50:50 please turn to page 312
If you would like to use your Ask The Audience please turn to page 328
Turn to the answer section on page 338 to find out if you've won £1,000,000!

15 ◆ £1,000,000 DOMESTIC

1

Pretiumque et causa laboris is the motto of which club?

- A: Birmingham City
- B: Blackburn Rovers
- C: Bolton Wanderers
- D: Burnley

2

Against which country did Alan Shearer play his last game for England?

- A: Romania
- B: Germany
- C: Portugal
- D: Ukraine

3

In the 2009/10 season, which manager employed his father as a freelance scout?

- A: David Moyes
- B: Steve Bruce
- C: Gary Megson
- D: Roy Hodgson

If you would like to use your 50:50 please turn to page 312
If you would like to use your Ask The Audience please turn to page 328
Turn to the answer section on page 338 to find out if you've won £1,000,000!

50:50

£100

World Cup

1 Options remaining are B and C
2 Options remaining are A and D
3 Options remaining are C and D
4 Options remaining are C and D
5 Options remaining are A and D
6 Options remaining are A and C
7 Options remaining are A and D
8 Options remaining are C and D
9 Options remaining are A and B
10 Options remaining are B and D
11 Options remaining are A and D
12 Options remaining are A and C
13 Options remaining are A and D
14 Options remaining are A and C
15 Options remaining are C and D
16 Options remaining are A and B
17 Options remaining are C and A
18 Options remaining are B and D
19 Options remaining are A and D
20 Options remaining are A and D
21 Options remaining are A and D
22 Options remaining are B and C
23 Options remaining are A and C
24 Options remaining are A and B
25 Options remaining are A and C
26 Options remaining are C and D
27 Options remaining are B and C
28 Options remaining are A and B
29 Options remaining are A and D
30 Options remaining are A and D
31 Options remaining are A and D
32 Options remaining are A and D
33 Options remaining are B and C
34 Options remaining are B and D
35 Options remaining are A and D
36 Options remaining are B and D
37 Options remaining are B and D
38 Options remaining are B and C
39 Options remaining are A and D
40 Options remaining are B and C
41 Options remaining are B and D
42 Options remaining are A and C
43 Options remaining are B and C
44 Options remaining are A and D
45 Options remaining are C and D
46 Options remaining are A and C
47 Options remaining are A and D
48 Options remaining are B and C
49 Options remaining are C and D
50 Options remaining are A and C

European

1 Options remaining are A and D
2 Options remaining are A and D
3 Options remaining are A and B
4 Options remaining are C and D
5 Options remaining are A and C
6 Options remaining are A and D

50:50

7 Options remaining are A and D
8 Options remaining are B and D
9 Options remaining are B and C
10 Options remaining are B and C
11 Options remaining are B and D
12 Options remaining are A and B
13 Options remaining are B and C
14 Options remaining are B and D
15 Options remaining are A and D
16 Options remaining are A and B
17 Options remaining are B and D
18 Options remaining are B and D
19 Options remaining are A and C
20 Options remaining are A and C
21 Options remaining are A and D
22 Options remaining are C and D
23 Options remaining are A and C
24 Options remaining are A and C
25 Options remaining are A and B
26 Options remaining are B and C
27 Options remaining are B and C

Domestic

1 Options remaining are B and D
2 Options remaining are B and D
3 Options remaining are A and C
4 Options remaining are B and C
5 Options remaining are A and C
6 Options remaining are C and D
7 Options remaining are A and D
8 Options remaining are A and C
9 Options remaining are A and B
10 Options remaining are A and C
11 Options remaining are A and C
12 Options remaining are A and D
13 Options remaining are A and B
14 Options remaining are B and C
15 Options remaining are A and C
16 Options remaining are B and C
17 Options remaining are A and D
18 Options remaining are A and B
19 Options remaining are A and D
20 Options remaining are B and C
21 Options remaining are C and D
22 Options remaining are B and D
23 Options remaining are C and D
24 Options remaining are B and C
25 Options remaining are A and D
26 Options remaining are A and C
27 Options remaining are A and D

50:50

£200

World Cup

1 Options remaining are C and D
2 Options remaining are A and D
3 Options remaining are B and D
4 Options remaining are A and C
5 Options remaining are B and D
6 Options remaining are B and D
7 Options remaining are A and D
8 Options remaining are B and D
9 Options remaining are B and C
10 Options remaining are B and C
11 Options remaining are A and D
12 Options remaining are B and D
13 Options remaining are A and B
14 Options remaining are A and D
15 Options remaining are B and D
16 Options remaining are A and C
17 Options remaining are A and D
18 Options remaining are B and C
19 Options remaining are A and B
20 Options remaining are C and D
21 Options remaining are A and B
22 Options remaining are B and D
23 Options remaining are A and C
24 Options remaining are C and D
25 Options remaining are A and D
26 Options remaining are B and C
27 Options remaining are A and B
28 Options remaining are C and D
29 Options remaining are C and D
30 Options remaining are B and D
31 Options remaining are B and D
32 Options remaining are B and C
33 Options remaining are A and B
34 Options remaining are A and D
35 Options remaining are A and C
36 Options remaining are B and C
37 Options remaining are A and D
38 Options remaining are A and B
39 Options remaining are A and C
40 Options remaining are D and C
41 Options remaining are A and D
42 Options remaining are C and D
43 Options remaining are A and B
44 Options remaining are C and D
45 Options remaining are B and D
46 Options remaining are A and D
47 Options remaining are A and C
48 Options remaining are B and D
49 Options remaining are B and D
50 Options remaining are C and D

European

1 Options remaining are C and D
2 Options remaining are A and D
3 Options remaining are B and C
4 Options remaining are C and D
5 Options remaining are A and D
6 Options remaining are B and C
7 Options remaining are C and D
8 Options remaining are A and C
9 Options remaining are B and C
10 Options remaining are C and D
11 Options remaining are A and B
12 Options remaining are A and D
13 Options remaining are A and C
14 Options remaining are B and C

50:50

15 Options remaining are B and C
16 Options remaining are B and C
17 Options remaining are C and D
18 Options remaining are C and D
19 Options remaining are C and D
20 Options remaining are C and D
21 Options remaining are A and D
22 Options remaining are A and B
23 Options remaining are A and D
24 Options remaining are B and C
25 Options remaining are A and D

Domestic

1 Options remaining are C and D
2 Options remaining are C and D
3 Options remaining are A and D
4 Options remaining are C and D
5 Options remaining are A and B
6 Options remaining are A and D
7 Options remaining are B and C
8 Options remaining are A and C
9 Options remaining are A and B
10 Options remaining are B and C
11 Options remaining are C and D
12 Options remaining are B and D
13 Options remaining are A and D
14 Options remaining are B and C
15 Options remaining are C and D
16 Options remaining are A and B
17 Options remaining are A and C
18 Options remaining are B and C
19 Options remaining are A and C
20 Options remaining are B and D
21 Options remaining are B and D
22 Options remaining are A and D
23 Options remaining are B and C
24 Options remaining are A and B
25 Options remaining are A and B

50:50

£300

World Cup

1 Options remaining are B and D
2 Options remaining are A and C
3 Options remaining are B and C
4 Options remaining are B and C
5 Options remaining are B and C
6 Options remaining are B and D
7 Options remaining are B and D
8 Options remaining are A and C
9 Options remaining are C and D
10 Options remaining are A and C
11 Options remaining are B and D
12 Options remaining are A and C
13 Options remaining are A and D
14 Options remaining are A and C
15 Options remaining are B and C
16 Options remaining are B and D
17 Options remaining are A and C
18 Options remaining are A and D
19 Options remaining are A and C
20 Options remaining are A and D
21 Options remaining are A and B
22 Options remaining are A and B
23 Options remaining are B and D
24 Options remaining are A and D
25 Options remaining are B and D
26 Options remaining are A and D
27 Options remaining are B and D
28 Options remaining are B and D
29 Options remaining are B and C
30 Options remaining are B and A
31 Options remaining are A and C
32 Options remaining are B and D
33 Options remaining are B and C
34 Options remaining are A and C
35 Options remaining are C and D
36 Options remaining are B and C
37 Options remaining are A and B
38 Options remaining are B and D
39 Options remaining are B and D
40 Options remaining are B and D
41 Options remaining are B and D
42 Options remaining are C and D
43 Options remaining are C and D
44 Options remaining are A and D
45 Options remaining are C and D
46 Options remaining are B and D
47 Options remaining are C and D
48 Options remaining are B and D
49 Options remaining are C and D

European

1 Options remaining are A and D
2 Options remaining are B and C
3 Options remaining are A and D
4 Options remaining are A and D
5 Options remaining are B and C
6 Options remaining are B and C
7 Options remaining are C and D
8 Options remaining are B and D
9 Options remaining are B and C
10 Options remaining are A and D
11 Options remaining are C and D
12 Options remaining are B and D
13 Options remaining are C and D
14 Options remaining are B and D
15 Options remaining are C and D

16 Options remaining are B and D
17 Options remaining are A and D
18 Options remaining are A and D
19 Options remaining are A and D
20 Options remaining are A and B
21 Options remaining are B and C
22 Options remaining are A and C
23 Options remaining are B and D
24 Options remaining are A and C

Domestic

1 Options remaining are B and D
2 Options remaining are B and C
3 Options remaining are A and B
4 Options remaining are B and D
5 Options remaining are A and D
6 Options remaining are A and C
7 Options remaining are B and C
8 Options remaining are B and C
9 Options remaining are A and C
10 Options remaining are A and B
11 Options remaining are A and C
12 Options remaining are B and D
13 Options remaining are A and C
14 Options remaining are B and C
15 Options remaining are B and D
16 Options remaining are C and D
17 Options remaining are A and C
18 Options remaining are B and C
19 Options remaining are A and C
20 Options remaining are B and C
21 Options remaining are C and D
22 Options remaining are A and B
23 Options remaining are B and C
24 Options remaining are A and D

50:50

£500

World Cup

1 Options remaining are A and B
2 Options remaining are C and D
3 Options remaining are C and D
4 Options remaining are A and B
5 Options remaining are B and D
6 Options remaining are A and B
7 Options remaining are A and D
8 Options remaining are A and D
9 Options remaining are A and C
10 Options remaining are B and D
11 Options remaining are A and C
12 Options remaining are A and B
13 Options remaining are B and C
14 Options remaining are A and C
15 Options remaining are A and C
16 Options remaining are C and D
17 Options remaining are A and B
18 Options remaining are B and D
19 Options remaining are A and D
20 Options remaining are B and C
21 Options remaining are B and D
22 Options remaining are C and D
23 Options remaining are B and D
24 Options remaining are A and B
25 Options remaining are B and D
26 Options remaining are B and D
27 Options remaining are B and D
28 Options remaining are B and D
29 Options remaining are A and C
30 Options remaining are A and C
31 Options remaining are A and D
32 Options remaining are C and D
33 Options remaining are C and D
34 Options remaining are B and C
35 Options remaining are A and C
36 Options remaining are A and C
37 Options remaining are B and D
38 Options remaining are A and C
39 Options remaining are C and D
40 Options remaining are A and D
41 Options remaining are B and D
42 Options remaining are B and C
43 Options remaining are A and D
44 Options remaining are B and D
45 Options remaining are C and D
46 Options remaining are A and C
47 Options remaining are A and C

European

1 Options remaining are B and C
2 Options remaining are C and D
3 Options remaining are B and C
4 Options remaining are B and C
5 Options remaining are A and D
6 Options remaining are A and D
7 Options remaining are B and C
8 Options remaining are B and D
9 Options remaining are A and D
10 Options remaining are A and D
11 Options remaining are C and B
12 Options remaining are C and D
13 Options remaining are C and D
14 Options remaining are B and C
15 Options remaining are A and B
16 Options remaining are B and C
17 Options remaining are A and D

50:50

18 Options remaining are A and D
19 Options remaining are B and D
20 Options remaining are C and D
21 Options remaining are A and D
22 Options remaining are B and D
23 Options remaining are B and D

Domestic

1 Options remaining are B and D
2 Options remaining are A and B
3 Options remaining are A and B
4 Options remaining are A and C
5 Options remaining are B and D
6 Options remaining are B and C
7 Options remaining are B and D
8 Options remaining are C and D
9 Options remaining are B and D
10 Options remaining are C and D
11 Options remaining are B and C
12 Options remaining are C and D
13 Options remaining are B and C
14 Options remaining are B and C
15 Options remaining are B and C
16 Options remaining are A and C
17 Options remaining are C and D
18 Options remaining are A and B
19 Options remaining are A and D
20 Options remaining are B and D
21 Options remaining are C and D
22 Options remaining are C and B
23 Options remaining are A and D

50:50

£1,000

World Cup

1 Options remaining are B and D
2 Options remaining are B and C
3 Options remaining are B and C
4 Options remaining are B and D
5 Options remaining are A and D
6 Options remaining are B and D
7 Options remaining are A and C
8 Options remaining are C and D
9 Options remaining are C and D
10 Options remaining are B and C
11 Options remaining are C and D
12 Options remaining are B and C
13 Options remaining are A and D
14 Options remaining are A and D
15 Options remaining are B and D
16 Options remaining are A and D
17 Options remaining are A and C
18 Options remaining are B and C
19 Options remaining are C and D
20 Options remaining are B and C
21 Options remaining are A and D
22 Options remaining are A and D
23 Options remaining are A and D
24 Options remaining are A and D
25 Options remaining are A and C
26 Options remaining are A and C
27 Options remaining are A and C
28 Options remaining are C and D
29 Options remaining are C and D
30 Options remaining are A and B
31 Options remaining are A and D
32 Options remaining are A and C
33 Options remaining are A and C
34 Options remaining are B and D
35 Options remaining are C and D
36 Options remaining are A and C
37 Options remaining are B and C
38 Options remaining are B and C
39 Options remaining are A and D
40 Options remaining are C and D
41 Options remaining are B and D
42 Options remaining are A and B
43 Options remaining are B and C
44 Options remaining are C and D
45 Options remaining are A and B
46 Options remaining are B and D

European

1 Options remaining are A and D
2 Options remaining are A and C
3 Options remaining are B and D
4 Options remaining are C and D
5 Options remaining are A and C
6 Options remaining are A and D
7 Options remaining are C and D
8 Options remaining are A and D
9 Options remaining are A and D
10 Options remaining are A and B
11 Options remaining are A and B
12 Options remaining are C and D
13 Options remaining are B and D
14 Options remaining are B and D
15 Options remaining are A and D
16 Options remaining are A and C
17 Options remaining are C and D
18 Options remaining are A and D

50:50

19 Options remaining are C and D
20 Options remaining are C and D
21 Options remaining are B and D
22 Options remaining are A and C

Domestic

1 Options remaining are A and C
2 Options remaining are B and C
3 Options remaining are A and C
4 Options remaining are A and D
5 Options remaining are B and C
6 Options remaining are B and C
7 Options remaining are A and B
8 Options remaining are A and B
9 Options remaining are A and B
10 Options remaining are B and D
11 Options remaining are B and C
12 Options remaining are B and D
13 Options remaining are A and C
14 Options remaining are A and C
15 Options remaining are A and D
16 Options remaining are A and D
17 Options remaining are A and C
18 Options remaining are C and D
19 Options remaining are B and C
20 Options remaining are A and B
21 Options remaining are B and C
22 Options remaining are B and C

50:50

£2,000

World Cup

1 Options remaining are B and C
2 Options remaining are A and C
3 Options remaining are A and B
4 Options remaining are B and D
5 Options remaining are B and D
6 Options remaining are A and B
7 Options remaining are B and C
8 Options remaining are A and C
9 Options remaining are A and D
10 Options remaining are B and D
11 Options remaining are B and C
12 Options remaining are A and B
13 Options remaining are C and D
14 Options remaining are B and C
15 Options remaining are B and C
16 Options remaining are A and D
17 Options remaining are C and D
18 Options remaining are B and D
19 Options remaining are B and C
20 Options remaining are B and C
21 Options remaining are A and B
22 Options remaining are B and C
23 Options remaining are B and D
24 Options remaining are A and C
25 Options remaining are C and D
26 Options remaining are B and C
27 Options remaining are A and D
28 Options remaining are B and C
29 Options remaining are A and B
30 Options remaining are B and C
31 Options remaining are A and C
32 Options remaining are B and C
33 Options remaining are B and C
34 Options remaining are B and C
35 Options remaining are B and C
36 Options remaining are A and D
37 Options remaining are B and C
38 Options remaining are A and D
39 Options remaining are B and D
40 Options remaining are A and C
41 Options remaining are A and B
42 Options remaining are A and B
43 Options remaining are C and D
44 Options remaining are C and D

European

1 Options remaining are B and D
2 Options remaining are B and C
3 Options remaining are A and B
4 Options remaining are B and C
5 Options remaining are A and D
6 Options remaining are A and D
7 Options remaining are C and D
8 Options remaining are A and D
9 Options remaining are A and B
10 Options remaining are B and D
11 Options remaining are B and C
12 Options remaining are B and C
13 Options remaining are A and B
14 Options remaining are A and C
15 Options remaining are A and C
16 Options remaining are B and D
17 Options remaining are C and D
18 Options remaining are C and D
19 Options remaining are A and D
20 Options remaining are A and D

50:50

21 Options remaining are A and C
22 Options remaining are A and B

Domestic

1 Options remaining are A and D
2 Options remaining are C and D
3 Options remaining are A and C
4 Options remaining are A and C
5 Options remaining are C and D
6 Options remaining are A and D
7 Options remaining are A and D
8 Options remaining are B and D
9 Options remaining are B and C
10 Options remaining are B and C
11 Options remaining are A and D
12 Options remaining are A and B
13 Options remaining are A and D
14 Options remaining are B and D
15 Options remaining are C and D
16 Options remaining are A and D
17 Options remaining are C and D
18 Options remaining are A and C
19 Options remaining are B and C
20 Options remaining are A and C
21 Options remaining are A and D
22 Options remaining are B and C

50:50

£4,000

World Cup

1 Options remaining are B and D
2 Options remaining are A and D
3 Options remaining are B and D
4 Options remaining are A and C
5 Options remaining are C and D
6 Options remaining are A and C
7 Options remaining are A and C
8 Options remaining are A and C
9 Options remaining are A and C
10 Options remaining are C and D
11 Options remaining are A and B
12 Options remaining are A and C
13 Options remaining are A and D
14 Options remaining are C and D
15 Options remaining are A and D
16 Options remaining are B and C
17 Options remaining are A and C
18 Options remaining are B and C
19 Options remaining are B and C
20 Options remaining are B and C
21 Options remaining are A and C
22 Options remaining are A and D
23 Options remaining are A and D
24 Options remaining are A and D
25 Options remaining are A and D
26 Options remaining are B and C
27 Options remaining are A and C
28 Options remaining are A and C
29 Options remaining are A and D
30 Options remaining are A and C
31 Options remaining are A and B
32 Options remaining are A and C
33 Options remaining are A and C
34 Options remaining are C and D
35 Options remaining are A and B
36 Options remaining are A and B
37 Options remaining are B and C
38 Options remaining are A and D
39 Options remaining are A and C
40 Options remaining are C and D
41 Options remaining are B and C

European

1 Options remaining are C and D
2 Options remaining are B and C
3 Options remaining are A and B
4 Options remaining are B and C
5 Options remaining are A and B
6 Options remaining are C and D
7 Options remaining are A and C
8 Options remaining are A and B
9 Options remaining are A and B
10 Options remaining are B and D
11 Options remaining are A and B
12 Options remaining are C and D
13 Options remaining are C and B
14 Options remaining are A and D
15 Options remaining are C and D
16 Options remaining are B and D
17 Options remaining are B and C
18 Options remaining are A and D
19 Options remaining are A and B
20 Options remaining are B and D

Domestic

1 Options remaining are A and D

50:50

2 Options remaining are C and D
3 Options remaining are A and C
4 Options remaining are A and D
5 Options remaining are A and C
6 Options remaining are B and D
7 Options remaining are B and C
8 Options remaining are B and C
9 Options remaining are B and D
10 Options remaining are A and B
11 Options remaining are C and D
12 Options remaining are A and C
13 Options remaining are B and C
14 Options remaining are A and C
15 Options remaining are C and D
16 Options remaining are B and C
17 Options remaining are B and D
18 Options remaining are A and C
19 Options remaining are A and B
20 Options remaining are B and D

50:50

£8,000

World Cup

1 Options remaining are A and D
2 Options remaining are B and D
3 Options remaining are A and B
4 Options remaining are B and D
5 Options remaining are B and C
6 Options remaining are C and D
7 Options remaining are B and C
8 Options remaining are B and D
9 Options remaining are A and D
10 Options remaining are A and D
11 Options remaining are C and D
12 Options remaining are A and D
13 Options remaining are A and B
14 Options remaining are A and C
15 Options remaining are A and D
16 Options remaining are B and D
17 Options remaining are A and C
18 Options remaining are A and D
19 Options remaining are B and C
20 Options remaining are B and D
21 Options remaining are B and D
22 Options remaining are C and D
23 Options remaining are C and D
24 Options remaining are A and D
25 Options remaining are C and D
26 Options remaining are A and B
27 Options remaining are C and D
28 Options remaining are A and D
29 Options remaining are A and B
30 Options remaining are C and D
31 Options remaining are B and D
32 Options remaining are B and D
33 Options remaining are B and C
34 Options remaining are B and C
35 Options remaining are A and C
36 Options remaining are A and B
37 Options remaining are C and D
38 Options remaining are B and D

European

1 Options remaining are A and C
2 Options remaining are B and D
3 Options remaining are B and D
4 Options remaining are A and C
5 Options remaining are C and D
6 Options remaining are A and B
7 Options remaining are A and C
8 Options remaining are A and B
9 Options remaining are A and D
10 Options remaining are B and C
11 Options remaining are A and B
12 Options remaining are A and C
13 Options remaining are A and D
14 Options remaining are B and C
15 Options remaining are A and B
16 Options remaining are B and D
17 Options remaining are B and C
18 Options remaining are A and B
19 Options remaining are C and D

Domestic

1 Options remaining are B and C
2 Options remaining are B and C
3 Options remaining are B and D
4 Options remaining are B and D
5 Options remaining are A and D

50:50

6 Options remaining are B and C
7 Options remaining are B and D
8 Options remaining are B and C
9 Options remaining are A and C
10 Options remaining are B and C
11 Options remaining are A and D
12 Options remaining are B and D
13 Options remaining are A and D
14 Options remaining are A and D
15 Options remaining are B and C
16 Options remaining are A and B
17 Options remaining are B and C
18 Options remaining are B and C
19 Options remaining are B and D

50:50

£16,000

World Cup

1 Options remaining are A and D
2 Options remaining are C and D
3 Options remaining are A and D
4 Options remaining are C and D
5 Options remaining are A and D
6 Options remaining are C and D
7 Options remaining are A and B
8 Options remaining are A and C
9 Options remaining are B and D
10 Options remaining are A and C
11 Options remaining are A and B
12 Options remaining are B and C
13 Options remaining are C and D
14 Options remaining are C and D
15 Options remaining are A and C
16 Options remaining are B and C
17 Options remaining are A and D
18 Options remaining are B and C
19 Options remaining are B and C
20 Options remaining are A and B
21 Options remaining are A and C
22 Options remaining are A and B
23 Options remaining are C and D
24 Options remaining are A and B
25 Options remaining are A and C
26 Options remaining are A and C
27 Options remaining are B and C
28 Options remaining are A and D
29 Options remaining are A and C
30 Options remaining are B and C
31 Options remaining are B and C
32 Options remaining are C and D
33 Options remaining are A and B
34 Options remaining are B and D
35 Options remaining are A and C
36 Options remaining are C and D

European

1 Options remaining are A and D
2 Options remaining are A and B
3 Options remaining are B and D
4 Options remaining are A and D
5 Options remaining are A and C
6 Options remaining are C and D
7 Options remaining are A and C
8 Options remaining are C and D
9 Options remaining are A and D
10 Options remaining are B and C
11 Options remaining are C and D
12 Options remaining are C and D
13 Options remaining are C and D
14 Options remaining are A and D
15 Options remaining are B and D
16 Options remaining are A and B
17 Options remaining are B and D
18 Options remaining are B and C

Domestic

1 Options remaining are A and B
2 Options remaining are C and D
3 Options remaining are A and B
4 Options remaining are C and D
5 Options remaining are A and B
6 Options remaining are B and C
7 Options remaining are B and D
8 Options remaining are A and C

50:50

9 Options remaining are A and C
10 Options remaining are C and D
11 Options remaining are B and C
12 Options remaining are A and D
13 Options remaining are B and D
14 Options remaining are C and D
15 Options remaining are A and B
16 Options remaining are B and D
17 Options remaining are A and B
18 Options remaining are A and B

50:50

£32,000

World Cup

1 Options remaining are C and D
2 Options remaining are C and D
3 Options remaining are A and B
4 Options remaining are B and D
5 Options remaining are A and B
6 Options remaining are A and B
7 Options remaining are B and D
8 Options remaining are B and D
9 Options remaining are A and D
10 Options remaining are A and D
11 Options remaining are B and C
12 Options remaining are A and B
13 Options remaining are A and C
14 Options remaining are A and D
15 Options remaining are B and C
16 Options remaining are A and B
17 Options remaining are B and D
18 Options remaining are B and C
19 Options remaining are C and D
20 Options remaining are C and D
21 Options remaining are B and D
22 Options remaining are A and D
23 Options remaining are C and D
24 Options remaining are B and C
25 Options remaining are A and C
26 Options remaining are C and D
27 Options remaining are C and D
28 Options remaining are B and C
29 Options remaining are C and D
30 Options remaining are A and B
31 Options remaining are A and C

European

1 Options remaining are B and C
2 Options remaining are A and C
3 Options remaining are A and D
4 Options remaining are A and D
5 Options remaining are A and C
6 Options remaining are B and C
7 Options remaining are B and C
8 Options remaining are A and C
9 Options remaining are C and D
10 Options remaining are A and C
11 Options remaining are B and D
12 Options remaining are B and C
13 Options remaining are A and C
14 Options remaining are B and C
15 Options remaining are C and D

Domestic

1 Options remaining are C and D
2 Options remaining are B and C
3 Options remaining are B and C
4 Options remaining are C and D
5 Options remaining are A and B
6 Options remaining are C and D
7 Options remaining are A and C
8 Options remaining are A and D
9 Options remaining are A and D
10 Options remaining are B and D
11 Options remaining are A and B
12 Options remaining are B and D
13 Options remaining are A and B
14 Options remaining are C and D
15 Options remaining are C and D

50:50

£64,000

World Cup

1 Options remaining are C and D
2 Options remaining are A and B
3 Options remaining are A and D
4 Options remaining are B and D
5 Options remaining are A and C
6 Options remaining are B and C
7 Options remaining are B and C
8 Options remaining are A and D
9 Options remaining are B and C
10 Options remaining are B and D
11 Options remaining are A and C
12 Options remaining are A and C
13 Options remaining are C and D
14 Options remaining are A and B
15 Options remaining are B and C
16 Options remaining are B and D
17 Options remaining are A and C
18 Options remaining are C and D
19 Options remaining are B and C
20 Options remaining are A and C
21 Options remaining are B and C
22 Options remaining are A and D
23 Options remaining are C and D
24 Options remaining are A and B

European

1 Options remaining are A and D
2 Options remaining are B and D
3 Options remaining are A and B
4 Options remaining are B and D
5 Options remaining are A and D
6 Options remaining are B and C
7 Options remaining are C and D
8 Options remaining are C and D
9 Options remaining are B and C
10 Options remaining are B and C
11 Options remaining are B and D
12 Options remaining are A and D
13 Options remaining are A and C

Domestic

1 Options remaining are A and B
2 Options remaining are A and D
3 Options remaining are B and C
4 Options remaining are B and D
5 Options remaining are A and D
6 Options remaining are A and B
7 Options remaining are B and C
8 Options remaining are A and B
9 Options remaining are C and D
10 Options remaining are A and D
11 Options remaining are A and C
12 Options remaining are A and C
13 Options remaining are A and B

50:50

£125,000

World Cup

1 Options remaining are A and B
2 Options remaining are A and C
3 Options remaining are A and C
4 Options remaining are A and D
5 Options remaining are A and B
6 Options remaining are B and C
7 Options remaining are A and D
8 Options remaining are B and D
9 Options remaining are C and D
10 Options remaining are A and D
11 Options remaining are B and D
12 Options remaining are B and C
13 Options remaining are B and C
14 Options remaining are B and D
15 Options remaining are B and C
16 Options remaining are C and D
17 Options remaining are A and B
18 Options remaining are A and D

European

1 Options remaining are A and B
2 Options remaining are B and D
3 Options remaining are C and D
4 Options remaining are B and D
5 Options remaining are B and C
6 Options remaining are B and D
7 Options remaining are B and D
8 Options remaining are A and C
9 Options remaining are A and D
10 Options remaining are B and C

Domestic

1 Options remaining are B and C
2 Options remaining are A and D
3 Options remaining are B and D
4 Options remaining are A and D
5 Options remaining are C and D
6 Options remaining are B and D
7 Options remaining are C and D
8 Options remaining are A and C
9 Options remaining are A and C
10 Options remaining are B and C

50:50

£250,000

World Cup

1 Options remaining are C and D
2 Options remaining are A and C
3 Options remaining are A and C
4 Options remaining are B and C
5 Options remaining are A and C
6 Options remaining are A and B
7 Options remaining are B and D
8 Options remaining are A and D
9 Options remaining are B and D
10 Options remaining are B and D

European

1 Options remaining are C and D
2 Options remaining are A and B
3 Options remaining are C and D
4 Options remaining are B and C
5 Options remaining are C and D

Domestic

1 Options remaining are B and C
2 Options remaining are B and C
3 Options remaining are A and B
4 Options remaining are A and C
5 Options remaining are A and D

£500,000

World Cup

1 Options remaining are A and D
2 Options remaining are C and D
3 Options remaining are B and D
4 Options remaining are A and B
5 Options remaining are B and C
6 Options remaining are B and D
7 Options remaining are C and D
8 Options remaining are B and C
9 Options remaining are A and B

European

1 Options remaining are B and C
2 Options remaining are A and C
3 Options remaining are C and D
4 Options remaining are A and D

Domestic

1 Options remaining are B and D
2 Options remaining are C and D
3 Options remaining are A and D
4 Options remaining are A and D

50:50

£1,000,000

World Cup

1 Options remaining are C and D
2 Options remaining are B and D
3 Options remaining are B and C
4 Options remaining are A and D
5 Options remaining are A and B
6 Options remaining are A and D
7 Options remaining are B and C

European

1 Options remaining are B and C
2 Options remaining are A and C
3 Options remaining are A and B

Domestic

1 Options remaining are A and D
2 Options remaining are A and B
3 Options remaining are B and C

Ask The Audience

£100

World Cup

1	A 1	B 5	C 94	D 0
2	A 90	B 3	C 4	D 3
3	A 2	B 0	C 1	D 97
4	A 6	B 3	C 2	D 89
5	A 0	B 1	C 1	D 98
6	A 1	B 1	C 98	D 0
7	A 10	B 2	C 3	D 85
8	A 1	B 0	C 0	D 99
9	A 1	B 96	C 0	D 3
10	A 2	B 3	C 0	D 95
11	A 4	B 2	C 3	D 91
12	A 1	B 4	C 90	D 5
13	A 1	B 0	C 0	D 99
14	A 1	B 3	C 91	D 5
15	A 4	B 0	C 4	D 92
16	A 85	B 4	C 10	D 1
17	A 1	B 1	C 96	D 2
18	A 0	B 1	C 4	D 95
19	A 4	B 0	C 1	D 95
20	A 5	B 4	C 0	D 96
21	A 94	B 1	C 5	D 0
22	A 0	B 0	C 99	D 1
23	A 99	B 1	C 0	D 0
24	A 0	B 97	C 3	D 0
25	A 1	B 2	C 95	D 2
26	A 1	B 1	C 98	D 0
27	A 1	B 0	C 99	D 0
28	A 3	B 70	C 25	D 2
29	A 30	B 4	C 6	D 60
30	A 2	B 1	C 0	D 97
31	A 3	B 5	C 2	D 90
32	A1	B1	C3	D95
33	A0	B1	C99	D0
34	A 0	B 0	C 3	D 97
35	A 95	B 1	C 4	D 0
36	A 2	B 1	C 1	D 96
37	A 8	B 2	C 0	D 90
38	A 0	B 99	C 1	D 0
39	A 1	B 10	C 8	D 81
40	A 0	B 95	C 1	D 4
41	A 5	B 90	C 4	D 1
42	A 1	B 1	C 98	D 0
43	A 1	B 99	C 0	D 0
44	A 0	B 2	C 5	D 93
45	A 0	B 2	C 97	D 1
46	A 0	B 6	C 92	D 2
47	A 5	B 0	C 0	D 95
48	A 1	B 96	C 0	D 3
49	A 0	B 5	C 5	D 90
50	A 2	B 2	C 96	D 0

European

1	A 10	B 2	C 3	D 85
2	A 1	B 10	C 5	D 84
3	A 96	B 1	C 0	D 3
4	A 0	B 0	C 9	D 91
5	A 99	B 0	C 1	D 0
6	A 1	B 5	C 0	D 94
7	A 91	B 3	C 1	D 5
8	A 5	B 0	C 0	D 95
9	A 0	B 0	C 91	D 9
10	A 0	B 97	C 2	D 1
11	A 5	B 0	C 0	D 95
12	A 70	B 25	C 3	D 2

ASK THE AUDIENCE

13	A 4	B 5	C 90	D 1
14	A 0	B 1	C 1	D 98
15	A 92	B 0	C 4	D 4
16	A 96	B 2	C 0	D 2
17	A 1	B 99	C 0	D 0
18	A 6	B 0	C 2	D 92
19	A 97	B 0	C 2	D 1
20	A 95	B 0	C 0	D 5
21	A 3	B 5	C 5	D 87
22	A 9	B 1	C 90	D 0
23	A 99	B 0	C 0	D 1
24	A 91	B 0	C 0	D 9
25	A 6	B 92	C 0	D 2
26	A 5	B 0	C 90	D 5
27	A 10	B 4	C 85	D 1

Domestic

1	A 0	B 93	C 3	D 4
2	A 20	B 0	C 0	D 80
3	A 91	B 0	C 9	D 0
4	A 0	B 0	C 95	D 5
5	A 2	B 0	C 98	D 0
6	A 0	B 15	C 85	D 0
7	A 11	B 9	C 0	D 80
8	A 0	B 2	C 96	D 2
9	A 80	B 10	C 5	D 5
10	A 0	B 0	C 98	D 2
11	A 79	B 1	C 10	D 10
12	A 2	B 0	C 1	D 97
13	A 0	B 70	C 10	D 20
14	A 1	B 5	C 94	D 0
15	A 80	B 5	C 0	D 15
16	A 0	B 2	C 0	D 98
17	A 7	B 2	C 0	D 91
18	A 1	B 95	C 4	D 0
19	A 3	B 0	C 2	D 95
20	A 10	B 85	C 5	D 0
21	A 5	B 0	C 14	D 81
22	A 0	B 1	C 0	D 99
23	A 0	B 9	C 0	D 91
24	A 2	B 0	C 97	D 1
25	A 14	B 5	C 0	D 81
26	A 0	B 6	C 92	D 2
27	A 95	B 5	C 0	D 0

£200

World Cup

1	A 9	B 1	C 90	D 0
2	A 4	B 4	C 2	D 90
3	A 3	B 1	C 1	D 95
4	A 87	B 0	C 3	D 10
5	A 20	B 5	C 5	D 70
6	A 1	B 98	C 1	D 0
7	A 1	B 4	C 0	D 95
8	A 1	B 0	C 2	D 97
9	A 3	B 4	C 90	D 3
10	A 0	B 1	C 98	D 1
11	A 99	B 0	C 1	D 0
12	A 3	B 4	C 2	D 91
13	A 1	B 90	C 4	D 5
14	A 3	B 5	C 1	D 91
15	A 1	B 4	C 10	D 84
16	A 1	B 1	C 96	D 2
17	A 99	B 1	C 0	D 0
18	A 5	B 0	C 95	D 0
19	A 0	B 99	C 0	D 1
20	A 0	B 3	C 97	D 10
21	A 95	B 1	C 2	D 2
22	A 1	B 99	C 0	D 0
23	A 0	B 0	C 99	D 1
24	A 0	B 10	C 3	D 87
25	A 0	B 1	C 0	D 99

ASK THE AUDIENCE

26	A 1	B 1	C 95	D 3
27	A 0	B 99	C 0	D 1
28	A 3	B 0	C 0	D 97
29	A 5	B 0	C 90	D 5
30	A 0	B 4	C 0	D 96
31	A 4	B 0	C 5	D 91
32	A 8	B 2	C 90	D 0
33	A 95	B 4	C 0	D 1
34	A 10	B 1	C 8	D 81
35	A 95	B 4	C 0	D 1
36	A 0	B 2	C 93	D 5
37	A 98	B 0	C 2	D 0
38	A 5	B 90	C 1	D 4
39	A 0	B 5	C 93	D 2
40	A 0	B 1	C 99	D 0
41	A 5	B 4	C 1	D 90
42	A 5	B 0	C 0	D 95
43	A 95	B 1	C 4	D 0
44	A 0	B 0	C 1	D 99
45	A 2	B 2	C 1	D 95
46	A 5	B 4	C 1	D 90
47	A 0	B 0	C 97	D 3
48	A 4	B 95	C 1	D 0
49	A 0	B 1	C 0	D 99
50	A 2	B 1	C 2	D 95

European

1	A 14	B 0	C 0	D 86
2	A 96	B 1	C 0	D 3
3	A 4	B 91	C 2	D 3
4	A 0	B 1	C 4	D 95
5	A 60	B 20	C 10	D 10
6	A 10	B 1	C 89	D 0
7	A 0	B 0	C 95	D 5
8	A 98	B 1	C 1	D 0
9	A 10	B 11	C 75	D 4
10	A 20	B 0	C 5	D 75
11	A 97	B 0	C 2	D 1
12	A 6	B 0	C 5	D 89
13	A 0	B 0	C 95	D 5
14	A 0	B 90	C 5	D 0
15	A 5	B 0	C 95	D 0
16	A 0	B 92	C 4	D 4
17	A 15	B 0	C 15	D 70
18	A 6	B 0	C 82	D 12
19	A 19	B 10	C 0	D 71
20	A 5	B 0	C 90	D 5
21	A 5	B 0	C 0	D 95
22	A 98	B 0	C 2	D 0
23	A 67	B 0	C 3	D 30
24	A 1	B 3	C 96	D 0
25	A 88	B 1	C 1	D 10

Domestic

1	A 6	B 0	C 4	D 90
2	A 8	B 6	C 10	D 76
3	A 5	B 0	C 0	D 95
4	A 0	B 4	C 4	D 92
5	A 90	B 0	C 10	D 0
6	A 22	B 0	C 8	D 70
7	A 28	B 10	C 62	D 0
8	A 81	B 9	C 0	D 10
9	A 67	B 10	C 3	D 20
10	A 10	B 11	C 79	D 0
11	A 0	B 2	C 98	D 0
12	A 15	B 10	C 0	D 75
13	A 97	B 0	C 3	D 0
14	A 3	B 77	C 20	D 0
15	A 0	B 10	C 0	D 90
16	A 90	B 10	C 0	D 0
17	A 5	B 2	C 91	D 2
18	A 17	B 80	C 3	D 0

19	A 0	B 0	C 95	D 5
20	A 4	B 10	C 0	D 86
21	A 14	B 0	C 0	D 86
22	A 5	B 28	C 10	D 57
23	A 20	B 80	C 0	D 0
24	A 16	B 82	C 1	D 1
25	A 10	B 90	C 0	D 0

£300

World Cup

1	A 2	B 98	C 0	D 0
2	A 10	B 4	C 95	D 1
3	A 1	B 1	C 98	D 0
4	A 2	B 93	C 5	D 0
5	A 0	B 95	C 5	D 0
6	A 5	B 90	C 5	D 0
7	A 0	B 10	C 5	D 85
8	A 5	B 10	C 81	D 4
9	A 0	B 5	C 5	D 95
10	A 96	B 2	C 2	D 0
11	A 3	B 95	C 1	D 1
12	A 0	B 0	C 97	D 3
13	A 0	B 0	C 2	D 97
14	A 0	B 40	C 60	D 0
15	A 15	B 4	C 79	D 2
16	A 1	B 2	C 2	D 95
17	A 0	B 1	C 99	D 0
18	A 1	B 0	C 0	D 99
19	A 87	B 10	C 3	D 0
20	A 8	B 10	C 1	D 81
21	A 95	B 0	C 4	D 1
22	A 99	B 1	C 0	D 0
23	A 0	B 4	C 1	D 95
24	A 0	B 1	C 1	D 98
25	A 0	B 0	C 1	D 99
26	A 95	B 4	C 0	D 1
27	A 5	B 4	C 1	D 90
28	A 0	B 2	C 98	D 0
29	A 1	B 90	C 4	D 5
30	A 5	B 95	C 0	D 0
31	A 5	B 0	C 95	D 0
32	A 0	B 90	C 5	D 5
33	A 5	B 90	C 0	D 5
34	A 3	B 1	C 95	D 1
35	A 5	B 10	C 75	D 10
36	A 0	B 0	C 97	D 3
37	A 99	B 0	C 1	D 0
38	A 1	B 0	C 2	D 97
39	A 1	B 95	C 2	D 2
40	A 3	B 5	C 1	D 91
41	A 3	B 90	C 4	D 3
42	A 1	B 1	C 96	D 2
43	A 15	B 5	C 5	D 80
44	A 89	B 1	C 0	D 10
45	A 3	B 3	C 4	D 90
46	A 10	B 4	C 1	D 85
47	A 5	B 0	C 0	D 95
48	A 3	B 5	C 1	D 91
49	A 1	B 5	C 4	D 90

European

1	A 12	B 10	C 0	D 78
2	A 0	B 0	C 80	D 10
3	A 95	B 5	C 0	D 0
4	A 30	B 0	C 5	D 65
5	A 0	B 0	C 95	D 5
6	A 2	B 98	C 0	D 0
7	A 0	B 4	C 10	D 86
8	A 10	B 10	C 0	D 80
9	A 0	B 30	C 70	D 0
10	A 5	B 0	C 0	D 95
11	A 6	B 7	C 74	D 13
12	A 5	B 0	C 0	D 95
13	A 0	B 8	C 80	D 2

ASK THE AUDIENCE

14	A 8	B 60	C 12	D 20
15	A 0	B 0	C 5	D 95
16	A 1	B 98	C 0	D 1
17	A 77	B 0	C 3	D 20
18	A 93	B 0	C 7	D 0
19	A 6	B 20	C 4	D 70
20	A 95	B 0	C 5	D 0
21	A 6	B 6	C 88	D 0
22	A 80	B 15	C 5	D 0
23	A 0	B 5	C 0	D 95
24	A 0	B 0	C 99	D 1

Domestic

1	A 2	B 6	C 10	D 82
2	A 0	B 0	C 95	D 5
3	A 0	B 95	C 5	D 0
4	A 5	B 5	C 0	D 90
5	A 5	B 0	C 10	D 85
6	A 8	B 12	C 60	D 20
7	A 10	B 20	C 70	D 0
8	A 10	B 0	C 85	D 5
9	A 10	B 15	C 75	D 0
10	A 0	B 95	C 0	D 5
11	A 6	B 2	C 92	D 0
12	A 3	B 6	C 4	D 87
13	A 67	B 0	C 0	D 33
14	A 19	B 81	C 0	D 0
15	A 0	B 25	C 25	D 50
16	A 0	B 5	C 71	D 24
17	A 2	B 20	C 78	D 0
18	A 0	B 0	C 85	D 15
19	A 0	B 0	C 90	D 10
20	A 16	B 3	C 81	D 0
21	A 15	B 0	C 0	D 85
22	A 67	B 0	C 3	D 30
23	A 0	B 10	C 90	D 0
24	A 1	B 0	C 0	D 99

£500

World Cup

1	A 4	B 85	C 1	D 10
2	A 1	B 0	C 99	D 0
3	A 5	B 0	C 95	D 0
4	A 0	B 99	C 1	D 0
5	A 0	B 0	C 3	D 97
6	A 3	B 95	C 1	D 1
7	A 0	B 10	C 3	D 87
8	A 95	B 1	C 4	D 0
9	A 5	B 0	C 91	D 4
10	A 0	B 1	C 1	D 98
11	A 15	B 5	C 78	D 2
12	A 81	B 11	C 5	D 3
13	A 1	B 0	C 95	D 4
14	A 92	B 2	C 4	D 2
15	A 90	B 0	C 2	D 8
16	A 1	B 4	C 0	D 95
17	A 81	B 1	C 8	D 10
18	A 4	B 5	C 0	D 91
19	A 90	B 4	C 4	D 2
20	A 11	B 49	C 35	D 5
21	A 14	B 35	C 31	D 20
22	A 1	B 1	C 10	D 86
23	A 8	B 8	C 12	D 72
24	A 57	B 36	C 5	D 2
25	A 10	B 87	C 3	D 0
26	A 1	B 0	C 0	D 99
27	A 4	B 13	C 5	D 78
28	A 0	B 3	C 0	D 97
29	A 6	B 25	C 68	D 1
30	A 90	B 5	C 5	D 0
31	A 8	B 4	C 38	D 50
32	A 30	B 1	C 9	D 60
33	A 0	B 1	C 0	D 99
34	A 1	B 96	C 3	D 2
35	A 80	B 5	C 5	D 10

ASK THE AUDIENCE

36	A0	B10	C88	D2
37	A 3	B 5	C 0	D 92
38	A 4	B 6	C 89	D 1
39	A 0	B 1	C 1	D 98
40	A 4	B 4	C 31	D 61
41	A 3	B 0	C 0	D 97
42	A 25	B 1	C 73	D 1
43	A 23	B 1	C 6	D 70
44	A 4	B 10	C 5	D 81
45	A 28	B 2	C 2	D 68
46	A 15	B 5	C 60	D 20
47	A 90	B 3	C 4	D 3

European

1	A 5	B 95	C 0	D 0
2	A 10	B 10	C 0	D 80
3	A 5	B 80	C 5	D 10
4	A 20	B 0	C 80	D 0
5	A 15	B 15	C 0	D 70
6	A 1	B 10	C 0	D 89
7	A 0	B 52	C 5	D 43
8	A 28	B 5	C 5	D 62
9	A 80	B 15	C 5	D 0
10	A 98	B 0	C 1	D 1
11	A 5	B 0	C 90	D 5
12	A 38	B 5	C 0	D 57
13	A 5	B 0	C 0	D 95
14	A 20	B 30	C 50	D 0
15	A 20	B 10	C 60	D 10
16	A 5	B 15	C 75	D 5
17	A 70	B 10	C 15	D 5
18	A 90	B 0	C 5	D 5
19	A 0	B 80	C 15	D 5
20	A 38	B 5	C 5	D 52
21	A 75	B 15	C 5	D 5
22	A 2	B 6	C 0	D 92
23	A 25	B 15	C 0	D 60

Domestic

1	A 10	B 0	C 2	D 88
2	A 10	B 85	C 0	D 5
3	A 5	B 90	C 5	D 0
4	A 0	B 0	C 90	D 10
5	A 5	B 5	C 0	D 90
6	A 10	B 57	C 33	D 0
7	A 0	B 95	C 0	D 5
8	A 0	B 0	C 95	D 5
9	A 5	B 90	C 0	D 5
10	A 5	B 0	C 5	D 90
11	A 5	B 75	C 15	D 5
12	A 0	B 0	C 5	D 95
13	A 5	B 67	C 0	D 28
14	A 10	B 85	C 5	D 0
15	A 0	B 95	C 5	D 0
16	A 10	B 3	C 87	D 0
17	A 0	B 5	C 5	D 90
18	A 90	B 0	C 5	D 5
19	A 90	B 0	C 10	D 0
20	A 0	B 0	C 10	D 90
21	A 6	B 4	C 0	D 90
22	A 5	B 0	C 90	D 5
23	A 23	B 10	C 0	D 67

£1,000

World Cup

1	A 15	B 2	C 40	D 43
2	A 10	B 87	C 3	D 0
3	A 2	B 2	C 61	D 35
4	A 5	B 94	C 1	D 0
5	A 87	B 1	C 10	D 2
6	A 3	B 2	C 10	D 85
7	A 3	B 2	C 70	D 25
8	A 0	B 0	C 98	D 2
9	A 0	B 2	C 13	D 85
10	A 25	B 5	C 65	D 5

ASK THE AUDIENCE

11	A 32	B 14	C 40	D 14
12	A 3	B 6	C 89	D 2
13	A 4	B 3	C 2	D 91
14	A 95	B 2	C 0	D 3
15	A 2	B 10	C 3	D 85
16	A 3	B 3	C 4	D 90
17	A 2	B 28	C 68	D 2
18	A 1	B 85	C 1	D 12
19	A 1	B 0	C 1	D 98
20	A 32	B 38	C 16	D 14
21	A 8	B 38	C 4	D 50
22	A 89	B 3	C 2	D 6
23	A 89	B 6	C 2	D 3
24	A 72	B 8	C 12	D 8
25	A 96	B 2	C 2	D 0
26	A 57	B 2	C 5	D 36
27	A 77	B 3	C 13	D 7
28	A 8	B 20	C 55	D 17
29	A 25	B 15	C 23	D 37
30	A 19	B 61	C 9	D 11
31	A 16	B 7	C 27	D 50
32	A 76	B 12	C 11	D 1
33	A 62	B 13	C 5	D 20
34	A 12	B 46	C 2	D 40
35	A 4	B 26	C 53	D 17
36	A 2	B 4	C 89	D 5
37	A 31	B 15	C 38	D 16
38	A 5	B 59	C 15	D 21
39	A 31	B 26	C 17	D 26
40	A 1	B 2	C 97	D 0
41	A 7	B 84	C 6	D 3
42	A 9	B 42	C 13	D 36
43	A 29	B 3	C 51	D 17
44	A 1	B 4	C 89	D 5
45	A 20	B 30	C 24	D 26
46	A 5	B 10	C 21	D 64

European

1	A 90	B 5	C 0	D 5
2	A 0	B 20	C 80	D 0
3	A 10	B 10	C 5	D 75
4	A 5	B 0	C 95	D 0
5	A 0	B 0	C 95	D 5
6	A 80	B 0	C 20	D 0
7	A 0	B 1	C 1	D 98
8	A 20	B 0	C 20	D 60
9	A 95	B 0	C 0	D 5
10	A 95	B 5	C 0	D 0
11	A 10	B 80	C 5	D 5
12	A 2	B 0	C 4	D 94
13	A 10	B 10	C 14	D 66
14	A 0	B 95	C 5	D 0
15	A 90	B 5	C 5	D 0
16	A 50	B 0	C 25	D 25
17	A 0	B 0	C 95	D 5
18	A 6	B 0	C 5	D 89
19	A 20	B 0	C 80	D 0
20	A 0	B 10	C 80	D 10
21	A 5	B 90	C 0	D 5
22	A 5	B 33	C 57	D 5

Domestic

1	A 76	B 24	C 0	D 0
2	A 5	B 20	C 75	D 0
3	A 38	B 0	C 62	D 0
4	A 15	B 15	C 0	D 70
5	A 24	B 24	C 52	D 0
6	A 10	B 0	C 90	D 0
7	A 20	B 70	C 10	D 0
8	A 90	B 10	C 0	D 0
9	A 70	B 25	C 5	D 0
10	A 5	B 80	C 5	D 10
11	A 5	B 10	C 75	D 10
12	A 15	B 85	C 0	D 0

13	A 51	B 10	C 0	D 39
14	A 5	B 0	C 95	D 0
15	A 67	B 28	C 0	D 5
16	A 6	B 32	C 0	D 62
17	A 90	B 10	C 0	D 0
18	A 30	B 33	C 0	D 37
19	A 0	B 57	C 33	D 10
20	A 95	B 5	C 0	D 0
21	A 15	B 60	C 0	D 15
22	A 0	B 70	C 25	D 5

£2,000

World Cup

1	A 12	B 12	C 47	D 29
2	A 18	B 12	C 41	D 29
3	A 37	B 46	C 10	D 7
4	A 25	B 21	C 26	D 28
5	A 7	B 52	C 26	D 15
6	A 21	B 43	C 9	D 27
7	A 4	B 39	C 27	D 30
8	A 35	B 21	C 15	D 29
9	A 17	B 23	C 19	D 41
10	A 19	B 27	C 25	D 29
11	A 20	B 17	C 61	D 2
12	A 37	B 41	C 5	D 17
13	A 25	B 27	C 19	D 29
14	A 26	B 12	C 45	D 17
15	A 15	B 41	C 26	D 18
16	A 8	B 1	C 29	D 62
17	A 31	B 3	C 64	D 2
18	A 10	B 3	C 16	D 71
19	A 25	B 29	C 37	D 9
20	A 7	B 26	C 48	D 19
21	A 28	B 45	C 16	D 11
22	A 21	B 2	C 76	D 1
23	A 16	B 35	C 27	D 22
24	A 12	B 30	C 42	D 16
25	A 12	B 17	C 3	D 68
26	A 7	B 46	C 12	D 35
27	A 21	B 18	C 22	D 39
28	A 19	B 23	C 37	D 21
29	A 41	B 26	C 20	D 13
30	A 28	B 32	C 27	D 13
31	A 10	B 38	C 46	D 6
32	A 13	B 7	C 71	D 9
33	A 13	B 25	C 51	D 11
34	A 21	B 38	C 4	D 7
35	A 29	B 21	C 31	D 19
36	A 19	B 5	C 34	D 42
37	A 16	B 34	C 38	D 12
38	A 31	B 21	C 29	D 19
39	A 21	B 45	C 19	D 15
40	A 3	B 21	C 35	D 41
41	A 5	B 31	C 38	D 26
42	A 67	B 2	C 13	D 18
43	A 9	B 21	C 2	D 68
44	A 1	B 28	C 12	D 59

European

1	A 43	B 52	C 5	D 0
2	A 5	B 70	C 5	D 20
3	A 70	B 10	C 0	D 20
4	A 5	B 90	C 5	D 0
5	A 5	B 5	C 38	D 52
6	A 15	B 5	C 15	D 65
7	A 5	B 10	C 70	D 15
8	A 5	B 0	C 0	D 95
9	A 82	B 8	C 10	D 0
10	A 10	B 85	C 5	D 0
11	A 28	B 5	C 62	D 5
12	A 0	B 95	C 0	D 5
13	A 90	B 5	C 0	D 5

14	A 80	B 15	C 5	D 0
15	A 80	B 10	C 10	D 0
16	A 15	B 85	C 0	D 0
17	A 15	B 0	C 85	D 0
18	A 5	B 5	C 0	D 90
19	A 52	B 24	C 5	D 19
20	A 80	B 10	C 10	D 0
21	A 28	B 5	C 67	D 0
22	A 80	B 10	C 10	D 0

Domestic

1	A 52	B 5	C 38	D 5
2	A 23	B 5	C 10	D 62
3	A 80	B 15	C 0	D 5
4	A 0	B 5	C 95	D 0
5	A 25	B 5	C 0	D 70
6	A 0	B 10	C 0	D 90
7	A 65	B 10	C 5	D 20
8	A 15	B 70	C 15	D 0
9	A 10	B 80	C 5	D 5
10	A 0	B 15	C 70	D 15
11	A 10	B 5	C 10	D 75
12	A 33	B 48	C 0	D 19
13	A 76	B 19	C 0	D 5
14	A 10	B 90	C 0	D 0
15	A 5	B 5	C 62	D 28
16	A 10	B 5	C 0	D 85
17	A 15	B 15	C 52	D 18
18	A 5	B 0	C 90	D 5
19	A 5	B 0	C 90	D 5
20	A 5	B 0	C 85	D 10
21	A 15	B 0	C 19	D 66
22	A 15	B 5	C 80	D 0

£4,000

World Cup

1	A 15	B 48	C 6	D 31
2	A 71	B 8	C 14	D 7
3	A 27	B 26	C 16	D 31
4	A 39	B 12	C 35	D 14
5	A 30	B 23	C 31	D 16
6	A 31	B 16	C 32	D 21
7	A 35	B 8	C 46	D 11
8	A 61	B 5	C 8	D 26
9	A 6	B 17	C 75	D 2
10	A 10	B 9	C 35	D 46
11	A 25	B 37	C 23	D 15
12	A 89	B 5	C 4	D 2
13	A 50	B 7	C 16	D 27
14	A 5	B 4	C 89	D 2
15	A 59	B 5	C 21	D 15
16	A 10	B 26	C 37	D 27
17	A 16	B 24	C 39	D 21
18	A 9	B 43	C 21	D 27
19	A 7	B 26	C 52	D 15
20	A 20	B 17	C 61	D 2
21	A 41	B 37	C 5	D 17
22	A 16	B 28	C 19	D 37
23	A 8	B 1	C 29	D 62
24	A 9	B 25	C 29	D 37
25	A 27	B 16	C 22	D 35
26	A 7	B 12	C 46	D 35
27	A 41	B 26	C 20	D 13
28	A 61	B 11	C 9	D 19
29	A 17	B 9	C 19	D 55
30	A 43	B 11	C 32	D 14
31	A 11	B 61	C 9	D 19
32	A 14	B 32	C 43	D 11
33	A 22	B 9	C 67	D 2
34	A 11	B 24	C 46	D 19

ASK THE AUDIENCE

35	A 21	B 61	C 3	D 15
36	A 19	B 31	C 24	D 26
37	A 26	B 34	C 31	D 9
38	A 25	B 25	C 19	D 31
39	A 29	B 25	C 26	D 20
40	A 24	B 14	C 25	D 37
41	A 28	B 18	C 32	D 22

European

1	A 4	B 0	C 4	D 92
2	A 8	B 92	C 0	D 0
3	A 4	B 92	C 0	D 4
4	A 8	B 18	C 74	D 0
5	A 82	B 18	C 0	D 0
6	A 4	B 10	C 82	D 4
7	A 35	B 17	C 48	D 0
8	A 4	B 75	C 17	D 4
9	A 61	B 0	C 9	D 30
10	A 22	B 52	C 4	D 22
11	A 90	B 5	C 5	D 0
12	A 17	B 13	C 0	D 70
13	A 0	B 35	C 61	D 4
14	A 13	B 13	C 17	D 57
15	A 35	B 0	C 61	D 4
16	A 7	B 79	C 7	D 7
17	A 7	B 23	C 70	D 0
18	A 61	B 35	C 4	D 0
19	A 0	B 61	C 26	D 13
20	A 26	B 4	C 0	D 70

Domestic

1	A 0	B 30	C 0	D 70
2	A 4	B 0	C 96	D 0
3	A 0	B 0	C 96	D 4
4	A 82	B 0	C 0	D 18
5	A 78	B 8	C 0	D 13
6	A 40	B 7	C 0	D 53
7	A 4	B 92	C 4	D 0
8	A 17	B 73	C 0	D 10
9	A 7	B 0	C 28	D 65
10	A 0	B 87	C 8	D 5
11	A 18	B 4	C 4	D 74
12	A 30	B 15	C 30	D 25
13	A 17	B 48	C 30	D 5
14	A 5	B 15	C 62	D 18
15	A 15	B 37	C 43	D 5
16	A 0	B 10	C 85	D 5
17	A 5	B 0	C 0	D 95
18	A 5	B 19	C 57	D 19
19	A 42	B 10	C 38	D 10
20	A 10	B 5	C 0	D 85

£8,000

World Cup

1	A 19	B 25	C 22	D 34
2	A 14	B 36	C 25	D 25
3	A 3	B 65	C 21	D 11
4	A 10	B 47	C 28	D 15
5	A 25	B 65	C 1	D 9
6	A 1	B 29	C 67	D 3
7	A 28	B 48	C 5	D 19
8	A 38	B 44	C 1	D 17
9	A 22	B 7	C 19	D 52
10	A 19	B 23	C 11	D 47
11	A 24	B 12	C 27	D 37
12	A 27	B 19	C 19	D 35
14	A 34	B 24	C 17	D 23
15	A 22	B 18	C 29	D 31
16	A 27	B 19	C 23	D 29
17	A 38	B 27	C 19	D 16
18	A 24	B 26	C 23	D 27
19	A 17	B 47	C 28	D 8
20	A 21	B 43	C 27	D 9
21	A 30	B 41	C 22	D 7

ASK THE AUDIENCE

22	A 25	B 20	C 28	D 27
23	A 31	B 15	C 20	D 34
24	A 31	B 16	C 29	D 24
25	A 16	B 1	C 41	D 42
26	A 23	B 38	C 10	D 19
27	A 10	B 21	C 2	D 67
28	A 9	B 24	C 30	D 37
29	A 23	B 29	C 25	D 23
30	A 17	B 32	C 10	D 41
31	A 11	B 21	C 7	D 61
32	A 31	B 21	C 10	D 38
33	A 21	B 30	C 25	D 24
34	A 10	B 54	C 21	D 15
35	A 11	B 1	C 81	D 7
36	A 61	B 8	C 25	D 6
37	A 24	B 17	C 39	D 20
38	A 30	B 33	C 31	D 6

European

1	A 43	B 0	C 22	D 35
2	A 17	B 73	C 10	D 0
3	A 10	B 74	C 0	D 16
4	A 74	B 0	C 0	D 26
5	A 0	B 10	C 74	D 16
6	A 65	B 0	C 22	D 13
7	A 73	B 22	C 5	D 0
8	A 59	B 26	C 5	D 10
9	A 63	B 10	C 10	D 17
10	A 4	B 63	C 7	D 26
11	A 7	B 65	C 14	D 14
12	A 5	B 42	C 44	D 9
13	A 56	B 0	C 22	D 22
14	A 35	B 39	C 4	D 22
15	A 74	B 4	C 22	D 0
16	A 17	B 18	C 30	D 35
17	A 0	B 48	C 39	D 13
18	A 13	B 66	C 4	D 17
19	A 8	B 8	C 84	D 0

Domestic

1	A 8	B 8	C 84	D 0
2	A 0	B 65	C 4	D 31
3	A 17	B 9	C 4	D 70
4	A 13	B 7	C 5	D 75
5	A 74	B 7	C 15	D 4
6	A 13	B 65	C 22	D 0
7	A 0	B 22	C 0	D 78
8	A 0	B 61	C 23	D 17
9	A 4	B 13	C 52	D 31
10	A 14	B 43	C 35	D 8
11	A 13	B 22	C 4	D 61
12	A 22	B 43	C 13	D 22
13	A 7	B 0	C 19	D 74
14	A 7	B 4	C 32	D 57
15	A 17	B 70	C 0	D 13
16	A 0	B 74	C 26	D 0
17	A 35	B 4	C 57	D 4
18	A 7	B 74	C 4	D 15
19	A 30	B 65	C 0	D 5

£16,000

World Cup

1	A 7	B 12	C 35	D 46
2	A 27	B 22	C 16	D 35
3	A 43	B 11	C 32	D 14
4	A 15	B 21	C 61	D 3
5	A 46	B 24	C 19	D 11
6	A 22	B 9	C 67	D 2
7	A 43	B 32	C 11	D 14
8	A 61	B 19	C 11	D 9
9	A 15	B 52	C 7	D 26
10	A 37	B 29	C 23	D 9

ASK THE AUDIENCE

11	A 62	B 1	C 29	D 8
12	A 16	B 28	C 37	D 19
13	A 17	B 5	C 41	D 37
14	A 20	B 17	C 61	D 2
15	A 27	B 21	C 43	D 9
16	A 16	B 24	C 39	D 21
17	A 37	B 10	C 26	D 27
18	A 21	B 3	C 59	D 15
19	A 25	B 13	C 51	D 11
20	A 4	B 68	C 7	D 21
21	A 27	B 7	C 50	D 16
22	A 5	B 89	C 4	D 2
23	A 25	B 15	C 23	D 37
24	A 35	B 46	C 10	D 9
25	A 6	B 2	C 75	D 17
26	A 61	B 26	C 5	D 8
27	A 8	B 35	C 46	D 11
28	A 32	B 21	C 32	D 31
29	A 31	B 23	C 16	D 30
30	A 35	B 12	C 39	D 14
31	A 16	B 26	C 31	D 27
32	A 7	B 8	C 14	D 71
33	A 15	B 48	C 31	D 6
34	A 25	B 30	C 2	D 43
35	A 21	B 34	C 37	D 8
36	A 37	B 6	C 39	D 18

European

1	A 40	B 0	C 38	D 22
2	A 4	B 96	C 0	D 0
3	A 17	B 0	C 26	D 57
4	A 4	B 4	C 35	D 57
5	A 13	B 13	C 57	D 17
6	A 0	B 7	C 61	D 32
7	A 22	B 17	C 48	D 13
8	A 39	B 0	C 18	D 43
9	A 0	B 5	C 5	D 90
10	A 25	B 39	C 18	D 18
11	A 4	B 0	C 26	D 70
12	A 7	B 0	C 89	D 4
13	A 4	B 22	C 48	D 26
14	A 65	B 22	C 5	D 8
15	A 4	B 87	C 9	D 0
16	A 13	B 61	C 13	D 13
17	A 0	B 38	C 22	D 40
18	A 0	B 5	C 78	D 17

Domestic

1	A 82	B 9	C 0	D 9
2	A 4	B 10	C 82	D 4
3	A 82	B 4	C 10	D 4
4	A 8	B 26	C 5	D 61
5	A 0	B 48	C 22	D 30
6	A 0	B 57	C 17	D 26
7	A 8	B 5	C 0	D 87
8	A 8	B 35	C 57	D 0
9	A 91	B 0	C 0	D 9
10	A 35	B 4	C 39	D 22
11	A 4	B 57	C 17	D 22
12	A 4	B 0	C 39	D 57
13	A 4	B 17	C 22	D 57
14	A 17	B 22	C 18	D 43
15	A 70	B 4	C 0	D 26
16	A 8	B 5	C 0	D 87
17	A 87	B 0	C 5	D 8
18	A 0	B 74	C 13	D 13

£32,000

World Cup

1	A 27	B 22	C 30	D 21
2	A 30	B 21	C 37	D 12
3	A 38	B 19	C 29	D 14
4	A 19	B 22	C 29	D 30
5	A 14	B 72	C 5	D 9

ASK THE AUDIENCE

6	A 31	B 33	C 30	D 6
7	A 24	B 20	C 17	D 39
8	A 24	B 22	C 26	D 28
9	A 3	B 23	C 7	D 67
10	A 61	B 25	C 8	D 6
11	A 7	B 81	C 11	D 1
12	A 54	B 10	C 15	D 21
13	A 21	B 25	C 30	D 24
14	A 21	B 10	C 31	D 38
15	A 7	B 61	C 11	D 21
16	A 10	B 41	C 17	D 32
17	A 25	B 29	C 23	D 23
18	A 30	B 37	C 24	D 9
19	A 7	B 20	C 29	D 24
20	A 10	B 21	C 2	D 67
21	A 23	B 38	C 19	D 10
22	A 27	B 21	C 23	D 29
23	A 16	B 41	C 42	D 1
24	A 16	B 29	C 31	D 24
25	A 15	B 20	C 34	D 31
26	A 27	B 25	C 20	D 28
27	A 30	B 7	C 41	D 22
28	A 27	B 9	C 43	D 21
29	A 28	B 17	C 8	D 47
30	A 27	B 23	C 26	D 24
31	A 19	B 27	C 38	D 16

European

1	A 27	B 59	C 5	D 9
2	A 36	B 32	C 27	D 5
3	A 5	B 0	C 5	D 90
4	A 27	B 18	C 5	D 50
5	A 18	B 13	C 64	D 5
6	A 18	B 14	C 54	D 14
7	A 8	B 5	C 82	D 5
8	A 13	B 23	C 41	D 23
9	A 5	B 5	C 0	D 90
10	A 32	B 4	C 64	D 0
11	A 14	B 45	C 5	D 36
12	A 0	B 50	C 30	D 20
13	A 45	B 5	C 27	D 23
14	A 5	B 45	C 45	D 5
15	A 5	B 27	C 41	D 27

Domestic

1	A 14	B 0	C 9	D 77
2	A 0	B 68	C 27	D 5
3	A 39	B 43	C 0	D 18
4	A 9	B 14	C 4	D 73
5	A 18	B 36	C 32	D 14
6	A 14	B 18	C 32	D 36
7	A 41	B 0	C 50	D 9
8	A 14	B 4	C 23	D 59
9	A 27	B 27	C 5	D 41
10	A 23	B 59	C 9	D 9
11	A 50	B 22	C 14	D 14
12	A 9	B 27	C 0	D 64
13	A 59	B 0	C 23	D 18
14	A 5	B 5	C 50	D 40
15	A 14	B 27	C 50	D 9

£64,000

World Cup

1	A 25	B 20	C 26	D 29
2	A 25	B 31	C 25	D 19
3	A 26	B 31	C 9	D 34
4	A 24	B 19	C 26	D 31
5	A 1	B 28	C 44	D 27
6	A 26	B 15	C 44	D 15
7	A 18	B 1	C 62	D 19
8	A 68	B 5	C 20	D 7
9	A 23	B 14	C 51	D 12
10	A 4	B 30	C 32	D 34
11	A 17	B 31	C 44	D 8

12	A 53	B 34	C 13	D 0
13	A 1	B 22	C 11	D 66
14	A 60	B 25	C 3	D 12
15	A 4	B 59	C 37	D 0
16	A 36	B 4	C 20	D 40
17	A 14	B 35	C 46	D 5
18	A 18	B 5	C 40	D 37
19	A 30	B 22	C 40	D 8
20	A 1	B 28	C 44	D 27
21	A 34	B 5	C 45	D 16
22	A 1	B 44	C 1	D 54
23	A 28	B 21	C 44	D 7
24	A 16	B 55	C 26	D 3

European

1	A 14	B 27	C 27	D 32
2	A 14	B 32	C 27	D 27
3	A 55	B 8	C 23	D 14
4	A 5	B 45	C 32	D 18
5	A 23	B 31	C 5	D 41
6	A 41	B 5	C 45	D 9
7	A 41	B 5	C 54	D 0
8	A 9	B 5	C 27	D 59
9	A 27	B 5	C 45	D 23
10	A 4	B 55	C 41	D 0
11	A 27	B 19	C 9	D 45
12	A 23	B 0	C 23	D 54
13	A 33	B 31	C 27	D 9

Domestic

1	A 9	B 45	C 32	D 14
2	A 46	B 27	C 0	D 27
3	A 4	B 78	C 4	D 14
4	A 28	B 36	C 18	D 18
5	A 45	B 23	C 18	D 14
6	A 50	B 14	C 27	D 9

7	A 4	B 55	C 9	D 32
8	A 26	B 28	C 23	D 23
9	A 0	B 23	C 64	D 13
10	A 14	B 27	C 4	D 55
11	A 45	B 9	C 32	D 14
12	A 50	B 14	C 18	D 18
13	A 68	B 0	C 14	D 18

£125,000

World Cup

1	A 21	B 56	C 11	D 12
2	A 55	B 9	C 6	D 30
3	A 53	B 21	C 22	D 4
4	A 23	B 6	C 8	D 63
5	A 28	B 32	C 30	D 10
6	A 11	B 58	C 26	D 5
7	A 46	B 33	C 19	D 2
8	A 3	B 54	C 31	D 12
9	A 18	B 6	C 62	D 14
10	A 5	B 34	C 16	D 45
11	A 37	B 45	C 12	D 6
12	A 26	B 25	C 29	D 20
13	A 4	B 39	C 51	D 6
14	A 26	B 39	C 24	D 11
15	A 27	B 28	C 26	D 19
16	A 24	B 27	C 12	D 37
17	A 27	B 35	C 19	D 19
18	A 28	B 17	C 8	D 47

European

1	A 52	B 26	C 18	D 4
2	A 23	B 9	C 32	D 36
3	A 30	B 16	C 21	D 33
4	A 35	B 37	C 5	D 23
5	A 9	B 18	C 41	D 32
6	A 27	B 50	C 23	D 0

ASK THE AUDIENCE

7	A 18	B 0	C 5	D 77
8	A 9	B 18	C 50	D 23
9	A 41	B 36	C 9	D 14
10	A 18	B 36	C 41	D 5

Domestic

1	A 14	B 55	C 8	D 23
2	A 36	B 23	C 32	D 9
3	A 14	B 35	C 14	D 37
4	A 50	B 36	C 14	D 0
5	A 23	B 27	C 41	D 9
6	A 31	B 33	C 9	D 27
7	A 32	B 9	C 45	D 14
8	A 45	B 27	C 18	D 10
9	A 41	B 32	C 23	D 4
10	A 45	B 50	C 5	D 0

£250,000

World Cup

1	A 23	B 23	C 28	D 26
2	A 21	B 27	C 43	D 9
3	A 23	B 29	C 32	D 16
4	A 15	B 40	C 43	D 2
5	A 25	B 13	C 51	D 11
6	A 24	B 39	C 17	D 20
7	A 27	B 14	C 15	D 44
8	A 67	B 2	C 10	D 21
9	A 20	B 30	C 5	D 45
10	A 28	B 44	C 7	D 21

European

1	A 15	B 29	C 23	D 33
2	A 20	B 55	C 15	D 10
3	A 30	B 25	C 5	D 40
4	A 20	B 31	C 29	D 20
5	A 29	B 20	C 31	D 20

Domestic

1	A 25	B 40	C 20	D 15
2	A 10	B 25	C 40	D 25
3	A 45	B 10	C 30	D 15
4	A 35	B 20	C 30	D 15
5	A 35	B 25	C 20	D 20

£500,000

World Cup

1	A 27	B 19	C 19	D 35
2	A 25	B 25	C 34	D 16
3	A 19	B 11	C 29	D 41
4	A 34	B 22	C 25	D 19
5	A 7	B 16	C 40	D 37
6	A 14	B 25	C 0	D 61
7	A 6	B 27	C 47	D 20
8	A 39	B 51	C 6	D 4
9	A 37	B 14	C 24	D 25

European

1	A 15	B 10	C 50	D 25
2	A 65	B 10	C 10	D 15
3	A 30	B 10	C 45	D 15
4	A 40	B 25	C 20	D 15

Domestic

1	A 15	B 25	C 29	D 31
2	A 15	B 25	C 5	D 55
3	A 40	B 5	C 25	D 30
4	A 35	B 15	C 5	D 45

£1,000,000

World Cup

1	A 25	B 15	C 23	D 37
2	A 8	B 1	C 42	D 49
3	A 24	B 37	C 24	D 15

ASK THE AUDIENCE

4	A 61	B 29	C 5	D 5
5	A 7	B 69	C 19	D 5
6	A 0	B 7	C 45	D 50
7	A 11	B 16	C 60	D 13

European

1	A 5	B 75	C 5	D 15
2	A 10	B 20	C 55	D 15
3	A 5	B 50	C 15	D 30

Domestic

1	A 20	B 25	C 5	D 50
2	A 50	B 0	C 10	D 40
3	A 5	B 35	C 45	D 15

Answers

£100

World Cup

1 C	2 A	3 D	4 D	5 D
6 C	7 D	8 D	9 B	10 D
11 D	12 C	13 D	14 C	15 D
16 A	17 C	18 D	19 D	20 D
21 A	22 C	23 A	24 B	25 C
26 C	27 C	28 B	29 D	30 D
31 D	32 D	33 C	34 D	35 A
36 D	37 D	38 B	39 D	40 B
41 B	42 C	43 B	44 D	45 C
46 C	47 D	48 B	49 D	50 C

European

1 D	2 D	3 A	4 D	5 A
6 D	7 A	8 D	9 C	10 B
11 D	12 A	13 C	14 D	15 A
16 A	17 B	18 D	19 A	20 A
21 D	22 C	23 A	24 A	25 B
26 C	27 C			

Domestic

1 B	2 D	3 A	4 C	5 C
6 C	7 D	8 C	9 A	10 C
11 A	12 D	13 B	14 C	15 A
16 B	17 D	18 B	19 D	20 B
21 D	22 D	23 D	24 C	25 D
26 C	27 A			

ANSWERS

£200

World Cup

1 C	2 D	3 D	4 A	5 D
6 B	7 D	8 D	9 C	10 C
11 A	12 D	13 B	14 D	15 D
16 C	17 A	18 C	19 B	20 C
21 A	22 B	23 C	24 D	25 D
26 C	27 B	28 D	29 C	30 D
31 D	32 C	33 A	34 D	35 A
36 C	37 A	38 B	39 C	40 C
41 D	42 D	43 A	44 D	45 D
46 D	47 C	48 B	49 D	50 D

European

1 D	2 A	3 B	4 D	5 A
6 C	7 C	8 A	9 C	10 D
11 A	12 D	13 C	14 B	15 C
16 B	17 D	18 C	19 D	20 C
21 D	22 A	23 A	24 C	25 A

Domestic

1 D	2 D	3 D	4 D	5 A
6 D	7 C	8 A	9 A	10 C
11 C	12 D	13 A	14 B	15 D
16 A	17 C	18 B	19 C	20 D
21 D	22 D	23 B	24 B	25 B

£300

World Cup

1 B	2 C	3 C	4 B	5 B
6 B	7 D	8 C	9 D	10 A
11 B	12 C	13 D	14 C	15 C
16 D	17 C	18 D	19 A	20 D
21 A	22 A	23 D	24 D	25 D
26 A	27 D	28 B	29 B	30 B

ANSWERS

31 C	32 B	33 B	34 C	35 C
36 C	37 A	38 D	39 B	40 D
41 B	42 C	43 D	44 A	45 D
46 D	47 D	48 D	49 D	

European

1 D	2 C	3 A	4 D	5 C
6 B	7 D	8 D	9 C	10 D
11 C	12 D	13 C	14 B	15 D
16 B	17 A	18 A	19 D	20 A
21 C	22 A	23 D	24 C	

Domestic

1 D	2 C	3 B	4 D	5 D
6 C	7 C	8 C	9 C	10 B
11 C	12 D	13 A	14 B	15 D
16 C	17 C	18 C	19 C	20 C
21 D	22 A	23 C	24 D	

£500

World Cup

1 B	2 C	3 C	4 B	5 D
6 B	7 D	8 A	9 C	10 D
11 C	12 A	13 C	14 A	15 A
16 D	17 A	18 D	19 A	20 B
21 B	22 D	23 D	24 A	25 B
26 D	27 D	28 D	29 C	30 A
31 D	32 D	33 D	34 B	35 A
36 C	37 D	38 C	39 D	40 D
41 D	42 C	43 D	44 D	45 D
46 C	47 A			

European

1 B	2 D	3 B	4 C	5 D
6 D	7 B	8 D	9 A	10 A

11 C	12 D	13 D	14 C	15 B
16 C	17 A	18 A	19 B	20 D
21 A	22 D	23 D		

Domestic

1 D	2 B	3 B	4 C	5 D
6 B	7 B	8 C	9 B	10 D
11 B	12 D	13 B	14 B	15 B
16 C	17 D	18 A	19 A	20 D
21 D	22 C	23 D		

£1,000

World Cup

1 D	2 B	3 C	4 B	5 A
6 D	7 C	8 C	9 D	10 C
11 C	12 C	13 D	14 A	15 D
16 D	17 C	18 B	19 D	20 B
21 D	22 A	23 A	24 A	25 A
26 A	27 A	28 C	29 D	30 B
31 D	32 A	33 A	34 B	35 C
36 C	37 C	38 B	39 A	40 C
41 B	42 B	43 C	44 C	45 B
46 D				

European

1 A	2 C	3 D	4 C	5 C
6 A	7 D	8 D	9 A	10 A
11 B	12 D	13 D	14 B	15 A
16 A	17 C	18 D	19 C	20 C
21 B	22 C			

Domestic

1 A	2 C	3 C	4 D	5 C
6 C	7 B	8 A	9 A	10 B
11 C	12 B	13 A	14 C	15 A

16 D	17 A	18 D	19 B	20 A
21 B	22 B			

£2,000

World Cup

1 C	2 C	3 B	4 D	5 B
6 B	7 B	8 A	9 D	10 D
11 C	12 B	13 D	14 C	15 B
16 D	17 C	18 D	19 C	20 C
21 B	22 C	23 B	24 C	25 D
26 B	27 D	28 C	29 A	30 B
31 C	32 C	33 C	34 B	35 C
36 D	37 C	38 A	39 B	40 C
41 B	42 A	43 D	44 D	

European

1 B	2 B	3 A	4 B	5 D
6 D	7 C	8 D	9 A	10 B
11 C	12 B	13 A	14 A	15 A
16 B	17 C	18 D	19 A	20 A
21 C	22 A			

Domestic

1 A	2 D	3 A	4 C	5 D
6 D	7 A	8 B	9 B	10 C
11 D	12 B	13 A	14 B	15 C
16 D	17 C	18 C	19 C	20 C
21 D	22 C			

£4,000

World Cup

1 B	2 A	3 D	4 A	5 C
6 C	7 C	8 A	9 C	10 D
11 B	12 A	13 A	14 C	15 A
16 C	17 C	18 B	19 C	20 C

ANSWERS

21 A	22 D	23 D	24 D	25 D
26 C	27 A	28 A	29 D	30 A
31 B	32 C	33 C	34 C	35 B
36 B	37 B	38 D	39 A	40 D
41 C				

European

1 D	2 B	3 B	4 C	5 A
6 C	7 C	8 B	9 A	10 B
11 A	12 D	13 C	14 D	15 C
16 B	17 C	18 A	19 B	20 D

Domestic

1 D	2 C	3 C	4 A	5 A
6 D	7 B	8 B	9 D	10 B
11 D	12 C	13 B	14 C	15 C
16 C	17 D	18 C	19 B	20 D

£8,000

World Cup

1 D	2 B	3 B	4 B	5 B
6 C	7 B	8 B	9 D	10 D
11 D	12 D	13 A	14 A	15 D
16 D	17 A	18 D	19 B	20 B
21 B	22 C	23 D	24 A	25 D
26 B	27 D	28 D	29 B	30 D
31 D	32 D	33 B	34 B	35 C
36 A	37 C	38 B		

European

1 A	2 B	3 B	4 A	5 C
6 A	7 A	8 A	9 A	10 B
11 B	12 C	13 A	14 B	15 A
16 D	17 B	18 B	19 C	

ANSWERS

Domestic

1 C	2 B	3 D	4 D	5 A
6 B	7 D	8 B	9 C	10 B
11 D	12 B	13 D	14 D	15 B
16 B	17 C	18 B	19 B	

£16,000

World Cup

1 D	2 D	3 A	4 C	5 A
6 C	7 A	8 A	9 B	10 A
11 A	12 C	13 C	14 C	15 C
16 C	17 A	18 C	19 C	20 B
21 C	22 B	23 D	24 B	25 C
26 A	27 C	28 A	29 A	30 C
31 C	32 D	33 B	34 D	35 C
36 C				

European

1 A	2 B	3 D	4 D	5 C
6 C	7 C	8 D	9 D	10 B
11 D	12 C	13 C	14 A	15 B
16 B	17 D	18 C		

Domestic

1 A	2 C	3 A	4 D	5 B
6 B	7 D	8 C	9 A	10 C
11 B	12 D	13 D	14 D	15 A
16 D	17 A	18 B		

£32,000

World Cup

1 C	2 C	3 A	4 D	5 B
6 B	7 D	8 D	9 D	10 A
11 B	12 A	13 C	14 D	15 B

ANSWERS

16 B	17 B	18 B	19 C	20 D
21 B	22 D	23 C	24 C	25 C
26 D	27 C	28 C	29 D	30 A
31 C				

European

1 B	2 A	3 D	4 D	5 C
6 C	7 C	8 C	9 D	10 C
11 B	12 B	13 A	14 B	15 C

Domestic

1 D	2 B	3 B	4 D	5 B
6 D	7 C	8 D	9 D	10 B
11 A	12 D	13 A	14 C	15 C

£64,000

World Cup

1 D	2 B	3 D	4 D	5 C
6 C	7 C	8 A	9 C	10 D
11 C	12 A	13 D	14 A	15 B
16 D	17 C	18 C	19 C	20 C
21 C	22 D	23 C	24 B	

European

1 D	2 B	3 A	4 B	5 D
6 C	7 C	8 D	9 C	10 B
11 D	12 D	13 A		

Domestic

1 B	2 A	3 B	4 B	5 A
6 A	7 B	8 B	9 C	10 D
11 A	12 A	13 A		

ANSWERS

£125,000

World Cup

1 B	2 A	3 A	4 D	5 B
6 B	7 A	8 B	9 C	10 D
11 B	12 C	13 C	14 B	15 B
16 D	17 B	18 D		

European

1 A	2 D	3 D	4 B	5 C
6 B	7 D	8 C	9 A	10 C

Domestic

1 B	2 A	3 D	4 A	5 C
6 B	7 C	8 A	9 A	10 B

£250,00

World Cup

1 C	2 C	3 C	4 C	5 C
6 A	7 D	8 A	9 D	10 B

European

1 D	2 B	3 D	4 B	5 C

Domestic

1 B	2 C	3 A	4 A	5 A

£500,000

World Cup

1 D	2 C	3 D	4 A	5 C
6 D	7 C	8 B	9 A	

European

1 C	2 A	3 C	4 A

Domestic

1 D	2 D	3 A	4 D

ANSWERS

£1,000,000

World Cup

1 D	2 D	3 B	4 A	5 B
6 D	7 C			

European

1 B	2 C	3 B

Domestic

1 D	2 A	3 C

Score sheets

Write your name and the names of any other contestans in the space provided. Shade in each of the boxes lightly with a pencil once you or one of your fellow contestants has won the amount in that box. If you or any of the other contestants answer a question incorrectly and are out of the game, use a soft eraser to rub out the relevant boxes so that the final score is showing.

SCORE SHEET

	50:50		50:50
15	£1 MILLION	15	£1 MILLION
14	£500,000	14	£500,000
13	£250,000	13	£250,000
12	£125,000	12	£125,000
11	£64,000	11	£64,000
10	£32,000	10	£32,000
9	£16,000	9	£16,000
8	£8,000	8	£8,000
7	£4,000	7	£4,000
6	£2,000	6	£2,000
5	£1,000	5	£1,000
4	£500	4	£500
3	£300	3	£300
2	£200	2	£200
1	£100	1	£100

SCORE SHEET

....

50:50			50:50		
☐	☐	☐	☐	☐	☐

15	£1 MILLION	15	£1 MILLION
14	£500,000	14	£500,000
13	£250,000	13	£250,000
12	£125,000	12	£125,000
11	£64,000	11	£64,000
10	£32,000	10	£32,000
9	£16,000	9	£16,000
8	£8,000	8	£8,000
7	£4,000	7	£4,000
6	£2,000	6	£2,000
5	£1,000	5	£1,000
4	£500	4	£500
3	£300	3	£300
2	£200	2	£200
1	£100	1	£100

SCORE SHEET

50:50		50:50	
15	£1 MILLION	15	£1 MILLION
14	£500,000	14	£500,000
13	£250,000	13	£250,000
12	£125,000	12	£125,000
11	£64,000	11	£64,000
10	£32,000	10	£32,000
9	£16,000	9	£16,000
8	£8,000	8	£8,000
7	£4,000	7	£4,000
6	£2,000	6	£2,000
5	£1,000	5	£1,000
4	£500	4	£500
3	£300	3	£300
2	£200	2	£200
1	£100	1	£100